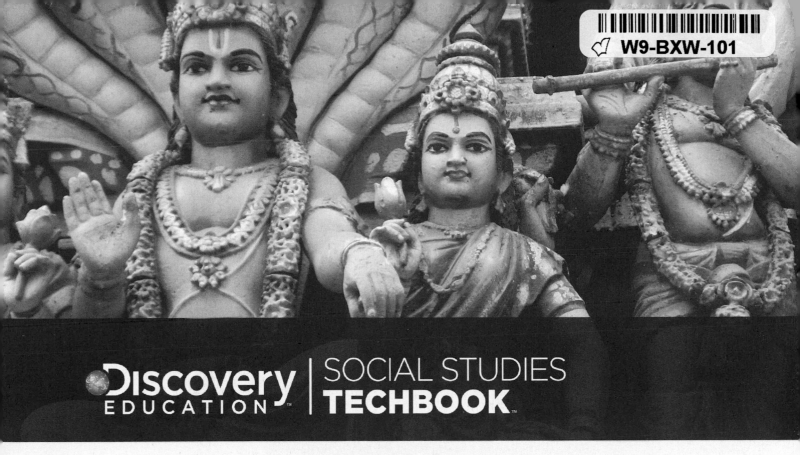

Discovery EDUCATION™ | SOCIAL STUDIES **TECHBOOK**™

ANCIENT WORLD HISTORY
CALIFORNIA EDITION

**Log in to Discovery Education
Social Studies Techbook
at DiscoveryEducation.com**

ISBN 13: 978-1-68220-235-7

Printed in the United States of America.

6 7 8 9 CWR 23 22 21 20 A

800-323-9084
4350 Congress Street, Suite 700, Charlotte, NC 28209
©2017 Discovery Education. All rights reserved.

Table of Contents

Letter to the Student

Dear Student,

Welcome to World History! You're about to begin an exciting journey into the world of Social Studies. There's more to world history than you might think. You will learn about the rise of civilizations, ancient civilizations, the growth of empires, and changes in Europe. Then, you will use what you have learned to analyze and understand present-day issues and propose solutions.

This resource is designed to use your reading and writing skills and prepare you for college, a career, and civic life.

Each lesson in this course is called a concept. Each concept has an Essential Question to guide your investigation of the main topic. The different tabs guide you through the lesson.

- ENGAGE: What do I know about this topic? What do I want to learn? Make connections between past and present learning as you dive into the concept.

- EXPLORE: Interact with text and multimedia as you explore key people, places, and events.

- EXPLAIN: Describe what you learned about the concept's topics and submit your answers online.

- ELABORATE: Examine primary sources, analyze complex problems, and complete activities to go deeper into the concept.

- EVALUATE: Review the concept's information with flashcards, quizzes, and writing assignments that help you express your position on critical topics.

Get ready to learn about the people, places, and ideas that have shaped World History.

The Discovery Education Team

Keep this resource handy as you explore the digital Techbook:

- **FLASHCARDS** for reviewing each concept's essential information
- **GRAPHIC ORGANIZERS** for taking notes on the Core Interactive Text
- **FOCUS QUESTIONS** for working through each concept
- **QR CODES** for connecting to Techbook pages and activities

Discovery Education Digital Connections

 Core Interactive Text: Explore an exciting combination of videos, photographs, audio recordings, interactive maps, and activities. A variety of reading tools, including highlighting, taking notes, two different text levels, text-to-speech, and Spanish translations will help you understand the text.

 Techbook Atlas: Use this interactive map to explore the human and physical geography of Earth with different overlays and base maps.

 Reference: View the definition and related media for key words and phrases.

 Global News: Watch exclusive videos that summarize the week's most pressing global news, through a Discovery Education partnership with trusted news leader MacNeil/ Lehrer Productions.

 Online Entry: Submit your answers online for EXPLAIN activities, and be sure to check the evaluation criteria or rubric before you do.

 Interactive Investigations: Found on the ELABORATE tab and other places, these activities challenge you to make critical decisions and study change over time through analyzing people, data, and places.

 Board Builder: Use images and text to create presentations with this handy tool.

UNIT 1: THE RISE OF CIVILIZATIONS (BEGINNINGS TO 5000 YEARS AGO)

Chapter 1: Human Origins

1.1 Rise of Humans

LESSON OVERVIEW

Lesson Objectives:

By the end of this lesson, you should be able to:

- **Explain the processes used by archaeologists to understand ancient history.**
- **Analyze the development of hominins in Africa and how their development relates to the rise of *Homo erectus* and draw conclusions about change over time.**
- **Connect patterns of early human settlement to the physical geography of settled regions.**

Key Vocabulary

artifact, Asia, bipedal, chronological, civilization, climate, culture, dig site, DNA, epoch, evolution, Fertile Crescent, fossil, genus, Giovanni da Verrazzano, Henry Hudson, hominin, *Homo sapiens*, Petra, savanna, scientific method, technology

Lesson Essential Question:

How do we learn about prehistoric societies?

FLASHCARDS

1 — Analyzing Artifacts

Archaeologists use sophisticated technology to investigate artifacts. The resulting evidence often causes scientists to modify old theories.

- Early archaeologists were often "treasure hunters" who kept few scientific records and did not exercise care with dig sites.
- Today, archaeologists work in teams and follow strict protocols in order to preserve both artifacts and sites.
- Archaeologists study the technology and culture of ancient civilizations to better understand how they lived.

Why Does It Matter?

Scientists studying behavior and material culture developed a new archaeology in the 1960s. The artifacts, or material remains of a culture, provide important clues about early civilizations. Such artifacts are often all that is available to archaeologists when investigating people and societies that did not have written records.

photo: Discovery Education
Archaeologists carefully study and record information about artifacts to better understand ancient people and civilizations.

2 — Hominins

The lifespan of the hominins extends from 5.8 million years ago to the present and includes a significant number of distinct species.

- Each subsequent hominin increased in height and brain size and became more adapted to walking rather than climbing.
- Well-substantiated theories can be replaced by new theories based on more current evidence.

Why Does It Matter?

Exploring hominins helps us understand more about modern humans. The discovery of *Homo erectus* solidified the theory that Africa is the birthplace of humanity.

photo: Library of Congress
Archaeological digs uncover evidence of early humans.

FLASHCARDS *(continued)*

3 ▸ Habitat and Environment

The ability of hominins to endure changes in their environment made them extremely adaptable, allowing them to exist for millions of years.

- Intense weather shifts that lasted for years limited hominins' options for places to live.
- Hominins learned to make tools and control fire as a means of surviving harsh environments.

Why Does It Matter?

The ability of hominins to adapt to the environment enabled them to survive and evolve. The search for habitable lands with plenty of natural resources caused hominins to spread out across the globe.

photo: Library of Congress

The earliest human remains have been found in the Rift Valley of Africa.

Name _____   **Date** _____

GRAPHIC ORGANIZER: Change Over Time Chart

Use this Change Over Time Chart to record information about how archaeology has changed over time. For supporting resources, go to The Rise of Civilizations > Human Origins > Rise of Humans > Explore > Archaeologists as Detectives.

Before:	After:

Changes:

Name _____ Date _____

GRAPHIC ORGANIZER: Comparison Chart

Use this Comparison Chart to compare what archaeologists have learned about ancient people and cultures, prehistory and hominins, and hominin habitats. For supporting resources, go to The Rise of Civilizations > Human Origins > Rise of Humans > Explore > Early Human Life.

Criteria	Ancient People and Cultures	Prehistory and Hominins	Hominin Habitats
What Have Archaeologists Learned About This Topic?			
How and Where Did Archaeologists Find Evidence?			

Name _____   Date _____

EXPLORE: FOCUS QUESTIONS

Using what you learned from the Core Interactive Text, answer each page's focus question:

Archaeologists as Detectives

How has the study of ancient humans changed over time?

_____
_____
_____
_____

Tools of the Craft

How do archaeologists examine a site?

_____
_____
_____
_____

Early Human Life

What have archaeologists learned about ancient people and cultures?

_____
_____
_____
_____

Hominin Prehistory and Hominins

What have archaeologists discovered about prehistory?

_____
_____
_____
_____

Hominin Habitats

Where did hominins settle?

_____
_____
_____
_____

PROJECTS AND ASSESSMENTS

Explain Activities

ACTIVITY TYPE: VISUALIZATION

Archaeological Investigation

In this investigation, you will think about the process of archaeological investigation. Working in a small group, you will list at least six important steps in the process. Then, you will fill in storyboard frames with drawings, sentence descriptions, or pictures that represent each step.

ACTIVITY TYPE: DIAGRAM

Rise of Humans

How do we learn about prehistoric societies? In this activity, you will answer this Essential Question by creating a mind map of the seven starred words and at least five other words or terms from the word bank. You also may add any other words or symbols of your choice. At the bottom of the page, you will write a summary of your mind map. Be prepared to share your thinking with classmates.

ACTIVITY TYPE: SOCIAL STUDIES EXPLANATION

Rise of Humans

In this Social Studies Explanation activity, you will use a template to assemble evidence from the sources you have explored. Then, you will write an answer to the Essential Question and defend your answer with supporting evidence.

Elaborate Activities

photo: Getty Images

INVESTIGATION TYPE: TIMELINE INQUIRY

The Earliest Humans

What were humans' earliest ancestors like, and how did their civilizations develop? In this activity, you will use the interactive Timeline Inquiry tool to learn how humans and their civilization evolved over many millions of years.

PROJECTS AND ASSESSMENTS *(continued)*

photo: Getty Images

ACTIVITY TYPE: ROLE PLAY

Mystery of the Red Queen

About 100 years ago, the mummy of an unknown woman, the "Red Queen," was discovered in the ruins of the ancient Mayan kingdom in the city of Palenque, Mexico. In this activity, you and a small group of classmates will role play a team of archaeologists trying to uncover the identity of the Red Queen and reveal more about the ancient Mayan kingdom. Then, you will compare your team's plan with the plan of actual archaeologists.

photo: Getty Images

ACTIVITY TYPE: STUDENT SLEUTH

The Neanderthals

In this activity, you will act as a museum curator who is creating an exhibit that shows an early Neanderthal settlement. You will examine an illustration of a Neanderthal settlement, compare the illustration to archaeologists' research results, and note any necessary changes that will make your museum display accurate. Finally, you will write an introductory paragraph for the museum exhibit to explain how the exhibit accurately portrays a Neanderthal settlement.

photo: Getty Images

ACTIVITY TYPE: DOCUMENT-BASED INVESTIGATION

A Modern Mystery: Amelia Earhart

In 1937, Amelia Earhart, one of the world's most famous pilots, disappeared under mysterious circumstances. What most likely happened to Earhart after taking flight in 1937? In this activity, you will use the archaeological process to discover what happened to her. Then, you will present your findings by writing a statement for a debate or writing a journal entry.

PROJECTS AND ASSESSMENTS *(continued)*

Evaluate Activities

BRIEF-CONSTRUCTED RESPONSE (BCR)

Rise of Humans

EXTENDED-CONSTRUCTED RESPONSE (ECR)

Rise of Humans

UNIT 1: THE RISE OF CIVILIZATIONS (BEGINNINGS TO 5000 YEARS AGO)

Chapter 1: Human Origins
1.2 Early Humans

LESSON OVERVIEW

Lesson Objectives:

By the end of this lesson, you should be able to:

- **Explain the migration patterns of early humans from Africa to various world regions.**
- **Identify and analyze the impact of early cultural developments on hunter-gatherer civilization.**
- **Identify and analyze the impact of early technological developments on hunter-gatherer civilization.**

Key Vocabulary

Africa, Bering Land Bridge, Beringia, Cro-Magnon, Euphrates River, Europe, Fertile Crescent, hunter-gatherer, Ice Age, migration, Neanderthal, New Stone Age, Oceania, Old Stone Age, Red Sea, region, Tigris River

Lesson Essential Question:

How did early humans improve their lives?

FLASHCARDS

1 Human Migration

As the global climate changed and the game they were dependent on moved to new areas, early hunter-gatherers migrated out of Africa and eventually spread to the Middle East, Asia, Oceania, and North and South America.

- Early humans left Africa for the Middle East and Asia when the African grasslands turned into a desert.
- Warmer temperatures encouraged modern humans to spread into Europe.
- Lower sea levels allowed humans to migrate from Siberia to Alaska over the Bering Land Bridge, and from China to Oceania.

Why Does It Matter?

Early humans moved from place to place as climates changed and existing habitats became less hospitable. This search for better environments and more resources inspired humans to spread to nearly every part of the world.

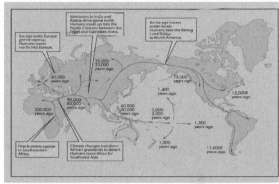

photo: Discovery Education
Humans reached North America by crossing the Bering Land Bridge.

2 The Hunter-Gatherer Life

Early humans used fire, weapons, and other increasingly complex tools to protect and care for the members of their social groups.

- The elderly and ill were cared for when they could no longer provide food for themselves.
- Tools included spears, stone blades, and chisels. Eyed needles were used for sewing garments.
- Stone blades were perfected by the Paleo-Indians of North America.
- Fire was crucial for hunting, defense, and warmth. Controlling fire was a major turning point in the development of human culture.

Why Does It Matter?

To meet the challenges in their lives, early hunter-gatherers developed social groups to support and help one another, which was the beginning of human society. Early humans created and developed tools, including fire, to hunt and provide for one another more effectively.

photo: Paul Fuqua
Early stone tools were often very simple, like this hand axe made from obsidian.

FLASHCARDS *(continued)*

3 ▶ Language and Art

The creation of social groups led to increased communication between early humans. *Homo sapiens* had the ability to speak and use language. This allowed for more complex interactions between individuals and groups. Modern humans also began to express themselves through art.

- The modern human larynx is lower and longer than those of apes or Neanderthals and allowed early modern humans to create the wide variety of sounds that make up language.
- Evidence of art has been found from as early as 35,000 years ago, and the quality of art remained unchanged for nearly 10,000 years after its first appearance.
- Cave paintings from this era often depicted animals.

Why Does It Matter?

Language and art were powerful tools used by early humans to communicate and pass knowledge to later generations. The creation of art, which requires time and effort from the artist, shows that humans had moved beyond simply struggling to survive and had begun to create culture.

photo: Pixabay

A painting from the Altamira caves. Early modern humans frequently painted animals.

Name _____ **Date** _____

GRAPHIC ORGANIZER: Visualization Chart

How did people migrate from Africa to other regions of the world? Use these frames to illustrate the events that led to migration of early humans from Africa to North America. For each step, include a visual and a description of that visual. For supporting resources, go to The Rise of Civilizations > Human Origins > Early Humans > Explore > From Africa to Southwest Asia, Europe, and Further into Asia.

Name _____ **Date** _____

GRAPHIC ORGANIZER: Visualization Chart *(continued)*

_____ _____ _____

_____ _____ _____

_____ _____ _____

_____ _____ _____

_____ _____ _____

_____ _____ _____

Name _____ **Date** _____

GRAPHIC ORGANIZER: GREASES Chart

Use this GREASES Chart to record information about early human societies' government, religion, economics, art and architecture, science and technology, environment, and social and cultural values. For supporting resources, go to The Rise of Civilizations > Human Origins > Early Humans > Explore > The Birth of Society.

Government	
Religion	
Economic	
Art & Architecture	
Science & Technology	
Environment	
Social & Cultural Values	

Name _____ Date _____

EXPLORE: FOCUS QUESTIONS

Using what you learned from the Core Interactive Text, answer each page's focus question:

From Africa to Southwest Asia, Europe, and Further into Asia
How did human populations spread?

_____
_____
_____
_____

Crossing the Ancient Seas
How did early humans travel to Oceania and North America?

_____
_____
_____

The Birth of Society
How did the formation of societies improve the lives of early humans?

_____
_____
_____

Hunting in Groups
How did living in groups improve early humans' ability to hunt?

_____
_____
_____

Making Tools
What improvements did early humans make to their tools as they migrated?

_____
_____
_____

Name _____ **Date** _____

EXPLORE: FOCUS QUESTIONS *(continued)*

Language
What effect did the development of speech and language have on human society?

_____

_____

_____

The Beginnings of Art
What purpose did art serve in early human society?

_____

_____

_____

PROJECTS AND ASSESSMENTS

Explain Activities

ACTIVITY TYPE: ADVERTISEMENT

Early Humans

In this activity, you will create an advertisement that shows how you would sell a tool to early human groups unfamiliar with the technology. Before creating the advertisement, use the graphic organizer to respond to questions.

ACTIVITY TYPE: DIAGRAM

Early Humans

Use at least 15 words from the word bank to create a graphic answer to the Essential Question. You may add other words or symbols, but you must use all of the starred words. Summarize your map at the bottom and be prepared to present your thinking.

ACTIVITY TYPE: SOCIAL STUDIES EXPLANATION

Early Humans

In this Social Studies Explanation activity, you will use a template to assemble evidence from the sources you have explored. Then, you will write an answer to the Essential Question and defend your answer with supporting evidence.

Elaborate Activities

photo: Associated Press

INVESTIGATION TYPE: TIMELINE MAP

The First Migrations

Where did the first humans settle, and how did their lives change over generations? Your mission is to examine the natural forces that drove early humans to migrate throughout the world and the cultural developments that came with that migration.

© Discovery Education | www.DiscoveryEducation.com

PROJECTS AND ASSESSMENTS *(continued)*

photo: Getty Images

ACTIVITY TYPE: SOCRATIC SEMINAR

Cave Art

Imagine you are an archaeologist. A museum has asked you to analyze examples of cave art and answer the question: Why was cave art created? Instead of coming up with one right answer, the museum wants you to present two plausible answers to this question. To prepare for this Socratic Seminar, you will analyze examples of cave art and watch video segments about cave art.

photo: Getty Images

ACTIVITY TYPE: EXPRESS YOUR OPINION

Early Human Hunting Expedition

In this activity, you will create a museum display illustrating the hunting practices of early humans. Use historical resources to write a description of the early human hunting expedition exhibit and create a drawing of the museum display. Support your depiction with historical evidence.

Evaluate Activities

BRIEF-CONSTRUCTED RESPONSE (BCR)

Early Humans

EXTENDED-CONSTRUCTED RESPONSE (ECR)

Early Humans

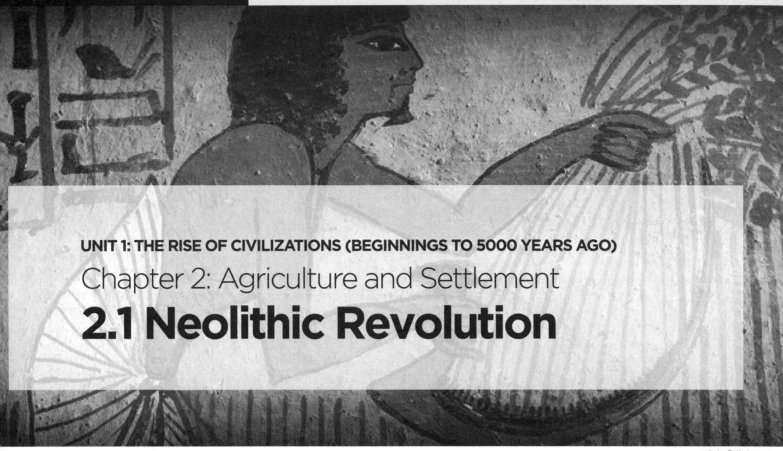

UNIT 1: THE RISE OF CIVILIZATIONS (BEGINNINGS TO 5000 YEARS AGO)

Chapter 2: Agriculture and Settlement

2.1 Neolithic Revolution

photo: Getty Images

LESSON OVERVIEW

Lesson Objective:

By the end of this lesson, you should be able to:

- **Analyze the impact of the Neolithic Revolution, which brought on the evolution from nomadic hunter-gatherer civilizations to the rise of stable, permanent civilizations.**

Lesson Essential Question:

In what ways did the agricultural revolution change human life?

Key Vocabulary

agricultural revolution, agriculture, Bronze Age, Çatalhöyük, Central Asia, cultivate, domestication, environment, Euphrates River, Fertile Crescent, hunter-gatherer, Iraq, Jericho, Jordan, Middle East, migration, Neolithic Period, Neolithic Revolution, nomadic, North Africa, pastoral, South America, surplus, Syria, Tigris River

Discovery EDUCATION | SOCIAL STUDIES TECHBOOK

Name _____ **Date** _____

EXPLORE: FOCUS QUESTIONS

Using what you learned from the Core Interactive Text, answer each page's focus question:

Why, Where, and When
Why did people begin to settle into permanent societies?

_____

_____

_____

The First Crops
How did farming develop during the Neolithic Revolution?

_____

_____

_____

The First Farm Animals
How did domestication of animals change society?

_____

_____

_____

Sophisticated Stone Tools
What tools did Neolithic people use?

_____

_____

_____

Name _____ Date _____

EXPLORE: FOCUS QUESTIONS *(continued)*

Birth of Cities
How did cities form?

_____
_____
_____

Farming Spreads Worldwide
How did farming spread?

_____
_____
_____

PROJECTS AND ASSESSMENTS

Explain Activities

ACTIVITY TYPE: ADVERTISEMENT

Neolithic Revolution

In this activity, you will create an advertisement to persuade a group of hunter-gatherers passing through your Neolithic community to stay and establish a settlement.

ACTIVITY TYPE: DIAGRAM

Neolithic Revolution

In what ways did the agricultural revolution change human life? In this activity, you will answer this Essential Question by creating a mind map that includes the eight starred words and terms from the word bank and at least four other words or symbols. Then, you will write a summary of your mind map and present it to the class.

ACTIVITY TYPE: SOCIAL STUDIES EXPLANATION

Neolithic Revolution

In this Social Studies Explanation activity, you will use a template to assemble evidence from the sources you have explored. Then, you will write an answer to the Essential Question and defend your answer with supporting evidence.

Elaborate Activities

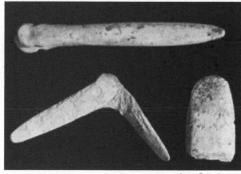

photo: Getty Images

INVESTIGATION TYPE: SOURCE ANALYSIS

Prehistoric Bone Tools

In what ways did the agricultural revolution change human life? In this investigation, you will answer the Essential Question by analyzing bone tools from Paleolithic culture and determining what the tools were made from and how the tools were used.

PROJECTS AND ASSESSMENTS *(continued)*

photo: Getty Images

ACTIVITY TYPE: CLASSROOM DEBATE

Genetic Modification

Is genetic modification a natural next step in the agricultural revolution? Should genetic modification be encouraged and supported? In this activity, you will examine the similarities and differences between modern genetic modification and the Neolithic Revolution and argue your stance on genetic modification in a debate.

photo: Paul Fuqua

ACTIVITY TYPE: ROLE PLAY

Impacts of Animal Domestication

How did the domestication of animals affect farmers? What complex effects did it have on human life? In this activity, you will analyze historical documents to determine the advantages and disadvantages of domesticating animals and use your findings to write an interview with two ancient farmers who explain which animals they chose to domesticate and why and describe how animal domestication has affected their lives and the lives of others.

Evaluate Activities

BRIEF-CONSTRUCTED RESPONSE (BCR)

Neolithic Revolution

EXTENDED-CONSTRUCTED RESPONSE (ECR)

Neolithic Revolution

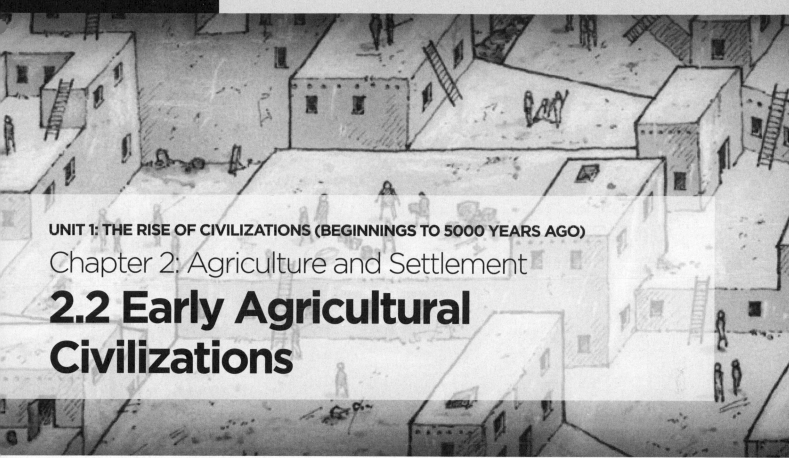

photo: Getty Images

UNIT 1: THE RISE OF CIVILIZATIONS (BEGINNINGS TO 5000 YEARS AGO)

Chapter 2: Agriculture and Settlement

2.2 Early Agricultural Civilizations

LESSON OVERVIEW

Lesson Objectives:

By the end of this lesson, you should be able to:

- Identify the characteristics of civilizations and connect these characteristics to the needs of settled society.
- Explain the cultural exchange among civilizations during this period.

Lesson Essential Question:

Why do humans form civilizations?

Key Vocabulary

agricultural revolution, agriculture, architecture, barter, capital, central government, city-state, civilization, climate, cultural region, culture, erosion, Euphrates River, harbor, levee, loess, natural resource, Nile River, nomadic, opportunity cost, productive resources, scarcity, specialization, supply and demand, Tigris River

FLASHCARDS

1 ▶ The Growth of Civilization

Agriculture enabled early humans to settle down in larger communities. As populations grew, elements of civilization begin to appear.

- **Agriculture provided a stable food source.**
- **Cities were supported by nearby farms. City dwellers could specialize in work areas they enjoyed.**
- **Specialization of labor created a social hierarchy.**
- **Central governments developed to organize the larger populations.**
- **Civilizations developed cultures that eventually included written languages.**

Why Does It Matter?

Agriculture provided the security that enabled early humans to settle into cities. The lifestyles possible in cities led to advances in technology and culture.

photo: Paul Fuqua

Agriculture changed the way ancient people lived, creating the possibility of civilization. What may have prompted people to begin farming?

2 ▶ Interactions Among Civilizations

Early Eurasian and African civilizations were located in areas that could support agricultural communities. Due to their proximity to one another, these civilizations exchanged goods and ideas.

- **Rivers were a source of water for crops, freshwater for drinking, and fish for food.**
- **Rivers provided a means of transportation.**
- **Geographic features like deserts, mountains, and oceans sometimes prevented civilizations from spreading.**
- **As they interacted, civilizations exchanged stories, technology, scientific knowledge, and religious ideas.**

Why Does It Matter?

Rivers and other bodies of freshwater made the development of civilization possible. The exchange of technology and ideas among civilizations boosted the advancement and spread of civilization.

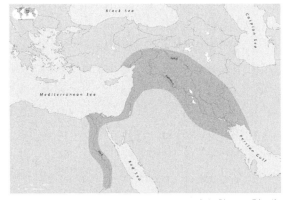

photo: Discovery Education

This map shows present-day Syria, Iraq, Turkey, and Jordan.

Name _____ **Date** _____

GRAPHIC ORGANIZER: GREASES Chart

Use this GREASES Chart to record information about early agricultural societies' government, religion, economics, art and architecture, science and technology, environment, and social and cultural values. For supporting resources, go to The Rise of Civilizations > Agriculture and Settlement > Early Agricultural Civilizations > Explore > Feed the People.

Government	
Religion	
Economic	
Art & Architecture	
Science & Technology	
Environment	
Social & Cultural Values	

Name _____ **Date** _____

GRAPHIC ORGANIZER: Main Idea Web

Use this Main Idea Web to record information about the geography of and interactions among early civilizations. For supporting resources, go to The Rise of Civilizations > Agriculture and Settlement > Early Agricultural Civilizations > Explore > The Importance of Geography.

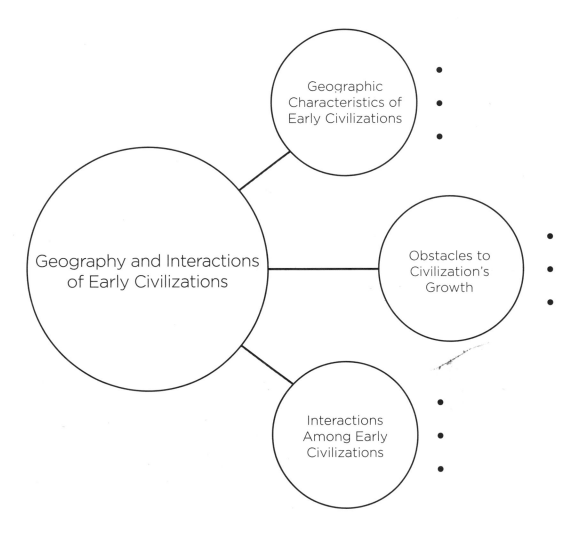

Name _____ Date _____

EXPLORE: FOCUS QUESTIONS

Using what you learned from the Core Interactive Text, answer each page's focus question:

Feed the People

Why was agriculture an essential step in the development of civilization?

_____

_____

_____

Specialization of Labor

What is the importance of specialization of labor in a civilization?

_____

_____

_____

The Creation of Social Classes

How did the specialization of labor impact society?

_____

_____

_____

Cities and Government

What are the roles of cities and central governments in civilization?

_____

_____

_____

Art and Architecture

What role did art and architecture play in the culture of early civilizations?

_____

_____

_____

Name _____ Date _____

EXPLORE: FOCUS QUESTIONS *(continued)*

Religion and Literature

What role did religion and written language play in the culture of early civilizations?

_____
_____
_____

The Importance of Geography

How did geography affect the establishment and spread of early civilizations?

_____
_____
_____

Exchanges Among Early Civilizations

What did civilizations exchange as they interacted?

_____
_____
_____

PROJECTS AND ASSESSMENTS

Explain Activities

ACTIVITY TYPE: ADVERTISEMENT

Early Agricultural Civilizations

In this activity, you will create an advertisement that sells either the Nile River Valley or the Fertile Crescent as the ideal location for a civilization.

ACTIVITY TYPE: MOVIE TRAILER

Early Agricultural Civilizations

Imagine a world where human beings live alone or in small groups. Isolated, scattered populations roam the land, until one day, The Civilization is born.

ACTIVITY TYPE: SOCIAL STUDIES EXPLANATION

Early Agricultural Civilizations

In this Social Studies Explanation activity, you will use a template to assemble evidence from the sources you have explored. Then, you will write an answer to the Essential Question and defend your answer with supporting evidence.

Elaborate Activities

photo: Getty Images

INVESTIGATION TYPE: SOURCE ANALYSIS

Early Settlements in Scotland

What can artifacts at early Scottish settlements reveal about early European culture and civilization? In this Source Analysis, your mission is to analyze images of Scottish settlements to understand the ancient culture and society of the region.

PROJECTS AND ASSESSMENTS *(continued)*

photo: Getty Images

ACTIVITY TYPE: ROLE PLAY

Digging Up the Past

In this activity, you will imagine that you are an archaeologist studying artifacts from an ancient civilization. Use the artifacts to draw conclusions about that civilization. Then, create a slideshow exhibit describing the culture.

photo: Getty Images

ACTIVITY TYPE: PITCH YOUR IDEA

The Best Layout for the City

In this activity, you will research the structure and layout of ancient cities. Then, you will use this research to pitch a proposal to the queen, explaining what you think is the best way to lay out her new city-state.

Evaluate Activities

BRIEF-CONSTRUCTED RESPONSE (BCR)

Agricultural Civilizations

EXTENDED-CONSTRUCTED RESPONSE (ECR)

Agricultural Civilizations

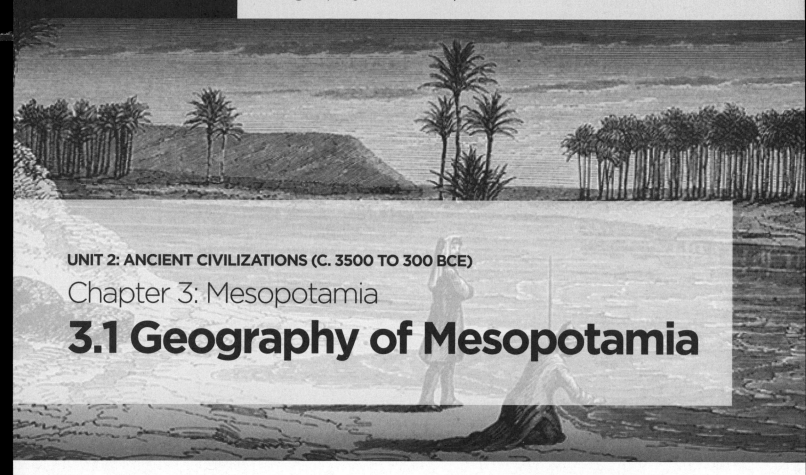

UNIT 2: ANCIENT CIVILIZATIONS (C. 3500 TO 300 BCE)

Chapter 3: Mesopotamia

3.1 Geography of Mesopotamia

LESSON OVERVIEW

Lesson Objectives:

By the end of this lesson, you should be able to:

- Locate ancient Mesopotamia and its important cities and rivers on a historical map and a modern map.

- Analyze the importance of the physical geography of Mesopotamia to the development of civilization.

- Identify and analyze the impact of agricultural innovations that led to the growth of cities in Mesopotamia.

- Explain the importance of trade to Mesopotamian civilization.

Key Vocabulary

agriculture, Akkadian Empire, Assyrian Empire, Baghdad, Canaan, city-state, civilization, climate, commerce, dam, dike, domestication, drought, empire, Eridu, Euphrates River, Fertile Crescent, goods, Harappa, hunter-gatherer, irrigation, levee, Mesopotamia, natural resource, nomadic, Persian Gulf, plain, plateau, scribe, silt, Sumer, textile, Tigris and Euphrates Rivers, Tigris River, trade, tradition-oriented economy, Ur, Uruk

Lesson Essential Question:

How did geography impact life in Mesopotamia?

FLASHCARDS

1 ▶ Location

Mesopotamia was one of the earliest urban civilizations. It was established around 3500 BCE in the valley between the Tigris River and the Euphrates River.

- **Mesopotamia was located where modern Iraq and eastern Syria are today.**
- **The Tigris and Euphrates Rivers were the two main rivers in Mesopotamia.**
- **Eridu, Ur, and Uruk were three of Mesopotamia's important cities. They were located along the Euphrates River.**

Why Does It Matter?

The cities of Mesopotamia were some of the first cities in the world. The Euphrates and Tigris Rivers played a large role in Mesopotamia's development.

photo: Discovery Education

Mesopotamia was established in the Fertile Crescent valley between the Tigris and Euphrates Rivers.

2 ▶ Land and Water

The soil of Mesopotamia was rich for crops, but the climate and annual floods were not suitable for farming.

- **Mesopotamians developed a system of irrigation to harness water from the Tigris and Euphrates Rivers.**
- **Irrigation provided water for crops year round.**
- **Annual floods destroyed crops and structures. Irrigation stopped the rivers from flooding.**
- **Through irrigation, the Mesopotamians produced a surplus of food.**

Why Does It Matter?

In order to become successful farmers, the Mesopotamians had to learn to use irrigation to control the floods from the Tigris and Euphrates Rivers. Doing so allowed their civilization to grow and flourish.

The Mesopotamians became successful farmers by creating an irrigation system to control the floods from the Tigris and Euphrates Rivers. Regulating the flow of water enabled the growth of the Mesopotamian civilization.

FLASHCARDS *(continued)*

3 Agricultural Innovations

Advances in agriculture allowed Mesopotamians to become more successful farmers.

- Irrigation provided necessary water to make farming easier.
- Mesopotamians invented a seeder plow. It allowed them to plow and plant at the same time.
- Mesopotamians domesticated animals. The animals were used for food and farm work.
- A surplus of food meant that not everyone had to farm. People could do other things for work.

Why Does It Matter?

Innovative farming techniques meant that more food was produced and fewer people needed to be farmers. There was enough food to feed entire cities and to trade for other goods and services. People came to the cities to trade and to do other jobs, and the civilization continued to grow.

photo: Paul Fuqua

Mesopotamians learned to control the rivers with levees and gates. They invented a seeder plow to plant their crops.

4 Trade

Mesopotamia did not produce all the resources it needed. However, it did produce an abundance of crops that could be used for trade.

- A system of trade began in the cities. Food was traded locally for other goods.
- Mesopotamians traded grains, oils, and textiles with outside societies for goods such as gems and wood.
- Merchants traveled to trading centers via land or sea. They used boats and donkeys to transport their goods.

Why Does It Matter?

Trade meant even more growth for Mesopotamia. Trading allowed Mesopotamians to meet all of their needs and establish a level of importance with outside cultures.

photo: Discovery Education

Trade in Mesopotamia came down to supply and need. What was produced in Mesopotamia could be traded for goods from other lands.

Name _____ **Date** _____

GRAPHIC ORGANIZER: Sequencing Chart

Use this Sequencing Chart to track the process by which mountain rains helped provide food in Mesopotamia. You may not need to use all of the boxes as you record your steps. For supporting resources, go to Ancient Civilizations > Mesopotamia > Geography of Mesopotamia > Explore > Locating Mesopotamia.

Step Title	Summary of Step	Significance

Name _____ **Date** _____

GRAPHIC ORGANIZER: Main Idea Web

Use this Main Idea Web to list geographic characteristics of each Mesopotamian city. For supporting resources, go to Ancient Civilizations > Mesopotamia > Geography of Mesopotamia > Explore > Big Cities.

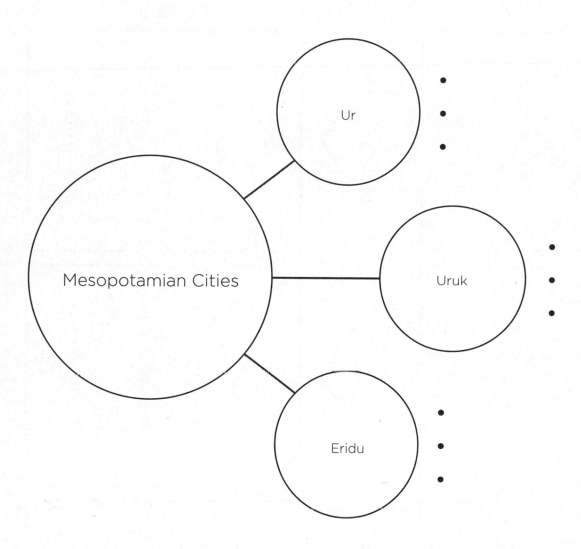

Name _____ **Date** _____

GRAPHIC ORGANIZER: Problem/Solution Chart

Use this Problem/Solution Chart to record details about the challenges that made large-scale farming difficult in Mesopotamia (the problems) and the specific technologies that the Mesopotamians utilized to deal with these challenges (the solutions). For supporting resources, go to Ancient Civilizations > Mesopotamia > Geography of Mesopotamia > Explore > Farming and Other Jobs.

Farming In Mesopotamia

Problem

A.

B.

C.

Solution

A.

B.

C.

© Discovery Education | www.DiscoveryEducation.com

Name _____ **Date** _____

GRAPHIC ORGANIZER: Main Idea Web

Use this Main Idea Web to record information about the purpose of trade in Mesopotamia and the characteristics of overseas and land trade. For supporting resources, go to Ancient Civilizations > Mesopotamia > Geography of Mesopotamia > Explore > Trade and Barter.

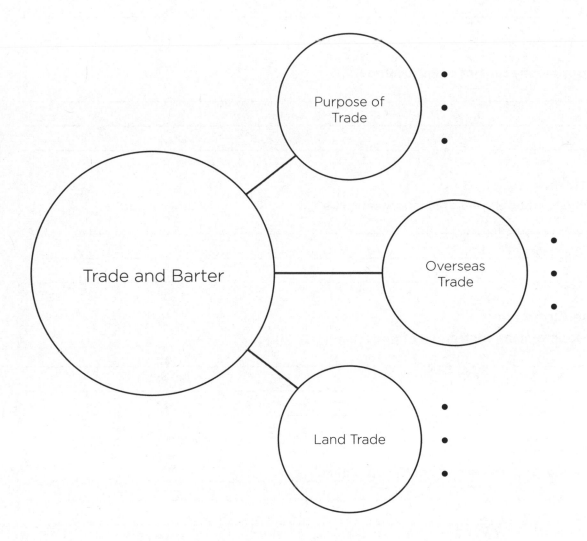

Name _____ Date _____

EXPLORE: FOCUS QUESTIONS

Using what you learned from the Core Interactive Text, answer each page's focus question:

Locating Mesopotamia
Where was ancient Mesopotamia?

_____
_____
_____
_____

Big Cities
Where were Mesopotamia's major cities located?

_____
_____
_____
_____

Resources and Geography
What was the physical geography of Mesopotamia like?

_____
_____
_____
_____

Controlling the Floods
How did the Mesopotamians control river floods?

_____
_____
_____
_____

Agricultural Innovations
What agricultural innovations came from Mesopotamia?

_____
_____
_____
_____

Name _____ Date _____

EXPLORE: FOCUS QUESTIONS *(continued)*

Farming and Other Jobs
How did farming advances make room for other jobs in Mesopotamia?

_____

_____

_____

Trade and Barter
How did trade become important in Mesopotamia?

_____

_____

_____

Overseas and Land Travel
How did Mesopotamians transport their goods to and from trade centers?

_____

_____

_____

PROJECTS AND ASSESSMENTS

Explain Activities

ACTIVITY TYPE: DIAGRAM

Geography of Mesopotamia

How did geography impact life in Mesopotamia? In this activity, you will answer the Essential Question by creating a mind map that includes the eight starred words and at least four more words from the word bank, as well as any other words or symbols you choose. At the bottom of your mind map, you will write a summary that explains your thinking. Then, you will present your mind map to the class.

ACTIVITY TYPE: ADVERTISEMENT

Mesopotamian Technology

In this activity, you will create an advertisement for a magazine, newspaper, website, television station, or radio station selling one of the following Mesopotamian technologies: levee, dam, seeder plow, guffa, or pavement. You will use the graphic organizer to identify the benefits and selling points of the technology. Then, you will incorporate those characteristics in an advertisement.

ACTIVITY TYPE: SOCIAL STUDIES EXPLANATION

Geography of Mesopotamia

In this Social Studies Explanation activity, you will use a template to assemble evidence from the sources you have explored. Then, you will write an answer to the Essential Question and defend your answer with supporting evidence.

Elaborate Activities

photo: Getty Images

INVESTIGATION TYPE: MAP-GUIDED INQUIRY

The Geography of Southwest Asia

How did geography influence the development of civilization in ancient Southwest Asia? In this investigation, you will use the Map-Guided Inquiry interactive tool to analyze the influences of geography on the ancient Southwest Asian civilization and examine how this region has changed over time.

PROJECTS AND ASSESSMENTS *(continued)*

photo: Library of Congress

ACTIVITY TYPE: CURRENT EVENTS
CONNECTION

Agriculture in the Central Valley

In this activity, you will compare farming in ancient Mesopotamia with farming in the Central Valley of present-day California. You will then write a proposal to the government board of the dry, arid region in which you live, explaining whether irrigation should be used for farming in the region and discussing the mixed costs and benefits of irrigation as an environmental control. You will support your opinion with evidence from the results of irrigation use in ancient Mesopotamia and in the Central Valley.

photo: Getty Images

ACTIVITY TYPE: PITCH YOUR IDEA

Urban Planning: Mesopotamian City

In this activity, you will imagine that you are an urban planner in ancient Mesopotamia. You will analyze sources to understand how Mesopotamian cities were organized and then use the information you gather to write rules for urban design in Mesopotamia. Then, you will use your rules to create your own map of a Mesopotamian city. Next, you will "pitch" your city plan by writing a persuasive paragraph or making a presentation that explains how your city makes the best use of the physical geography of the area and embodies the rules of urban design.

photo: Library of Congress

ACTIVITY TYPE: DOCUMENT-BASED
INVESTIGATION

Geography of Mesopotamia

How has agricultural technology changed since ancient Mesopotamia? How have these changes affected society? In this document-based investigation, you will answer these questions by creating a slideshow or a room layout map for a museum exhibit or by writing a brief essay that serves as the introduction to the museum exhibit. You will incorporate details from at least six of the document sources in your answer.

PROJECTS AND ASSESSMENTS *(continued)*

Evaluate Activities

 BRIEF-CONSTRUCTED RESPONSE (BCR)

Geography of Mesopotamia

 EXTENDED-CONSTRUCTED RESPONSE (ECR)

Geography of Mesopotamia

photo: Getty Images

UNIT 2: ANCIENT CIVILIZATIONS (C. 3500 TO 300 BCE)

Chapter 3: Mesopotamia

3.2 Mesopotamian Society

LESSON OVERVIEW

Lesson Objectives:

By the end of this lesson, you should be able to:

- Describe the religious beliefs and practices of ancient Mesopotamia.
- Describe the social structure—including gender divisions—of Mesopotamia and draw conclusions about its impact on the lives of Mesopotamians.
- Describe and map the cycles of conquest that led to the ascension of varied civilizations in Mesopotamia from 3000 to 500 BCE.

Lesson Essential Question:

How did religion and gender influence Mesopotamian society?

Key Vocabulary

Akkadian Empire, Akkadians, artisan, Assyrian Empire, Babylon, Babylonia, Babyloninan Empire, Chaldeans, city-state, civilization, Code of Hammurabi, code of law, culture, cuneiform, deity, division of labor, empire, Euphrates River, fertile, Gilgamesh, goods, Hammurabi, irrigation, Medes, merchant, Mesopotamia, Nebuchadnezzar, Neo-Babylonian Empire, patriarchal, polytheism, religion, Sargon, scribe, social pyramid, stylus, Sumer, Sumerians, Tigris and Euphrates Rivers, Tigris River, trade, ziggurat

FLASHCARDS

1 Mesopotamian Religion

Mesopotamians were polytheists who worshiped many different gods connected to nature and to particular aspects of life.

- Each Mesopotamian city had its own god that it worshiped.
- Mesopotamian city-states built ziggurats for worshiping their gods. Ziggurats had temples and altars to the gods, as well as long staircases for the gods to descend to Earth.
- Mesopotamians believed that their kings were chosen by the gods. The king and the priests were in charge of religious ceremonies that were conducted to please the gods.

Why Does It Matter?

Mesopotamia was one of the earliest civilizations to have an organized religion. Mesopotamians' religion helped shape their society and culture.

photo: Pixabay
Mesopotamians built ziggurats as temples to their gods.

2 A Social Pyramid

Mesopotamian social classes can be depicted in a social pyramid. People's level on the pyramid was determined by their profession. Although some social mobility occurred, most people stayed at the level into which they were born for their entire lives.

- The king was the primary political and religious figure.
- Priests and government officials directed the religious and administrative matters of the city-state.
- Artisans made the goods for the city-state. Merchants traded goods among city-states and between different ancient cultures. Scribes were the official record-keepers of society.
- Farmers grew the food that allowed the civilization to thrive. In return, they received protection from the king and support from the priests.
- Enslaved people were at the bottom of the social pyramid and had no power.

Why Does It Matter?

People from all levels of Mesopotamian society were important to the success of the civilization, although different groups had different amounts of power.

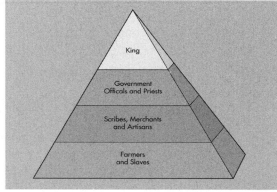

photo: Discovery Education
Mesopotamian society was organized into social classes that can be depicted in a social pyramid.

FLASHCARDS *(continued)*

3 ▶ **A Series of Conquests**

Mesopotamia was a rich land that many sought to conquer.

- Sumer was a loose group of city-states between the Tigris and Euphrates Rivers.
- The Akkadian Empire was the first major empire in Mesopotamia. Sargon was the first king of the Akkadian Empire.
- The Babylonian Empire conquered much of Mesopotamia after the collapse of the Akkadian Empire.
- The Assyrian Empire was the largest of the four empires. The Assyrians conquered other lands easily, but they had difficulty maintaining control of their vast empire.
- The Chaldean Empire's king, Nebuchadnezzar, was a ruthless conqueror, but he also organized many great building projects in the capital city of Babylon.

Why Does It Matter?

Because Mesopotamia had rich agricultural land and a vibrant culture, it was conquered by many different empires. Each new empire brought its own cultural aspects to Mesopotamia while also adopting certain aspects of the existing Mesopotamian culture.

photo: Discovery Education
Many different empires conquered Mesopotamia and took advantage of its riches.

Name _____ **Date** _____

GRAPHIC ORGANIZER: Vocabulary Chart

Use this Vocabulary Chart to define the word *polytheism*. For supporting resources, go to Ancient Civilizations > Mesopotamia > Mesopotamian Society > Explore > Religion in Mesopotamia.

DEFINITION: Personal:	EXAMPLES (Drawn or Written):
Techbook Reference:	

TERM: *polytheism*

SENTENCES: Teacher/Book:	RELATED:	WORD PARTS:
Personal:		

Outside of School (Who Would Use the Word? How Would He or She Use It?):

Name _____ Date _____

EXPLORE: FOCUS QUESTIONS *(continued)*

A Series of Empires (c. 2300–1595 BCE)
Who were the first rulers to unite Mesopotamia?

_____

_____

_____

A Series of Empires (c. 900–539 BCE)
What later empires ruled Mesopotamia?

_____

_____

_____

PROJECTS AND ASSESSMENTS

Explain Activities

ACTIVITY TYPE: DIAGRAM

Mesopotamian Social Pyramid

In this activity, you will complete a diagram of a Mesopotamian social pyramid with information about the various social classes. For each class, or level, in the diagram you will draw at least one picture and write three facts about that social class.

ACTIVITY TYPE: YOU AS JOURNALIST

Mesopotamian Society

In this activity, you, as a reporter, will write the transcript of your interview with the king of one of the Mesopotamian empires. Your interview questions should include why the king decided to conquer Mesopotamia, how he governs the society, and how he has contributed to the empire's growth.

ACTIVITY TYPE: SOCIAL STUDIES EXPLANATION

Mesopotamian Society

In this Social Studies Explanation activity, you will use a template to assemble evidence from the sources you have explored. Then, you will write an answer to the Essential Question and defend your answer with supporting evidence.

Elaborate Activities

photo: Getty Images

INVESTIGATION TYPE: SOURCE ANALYSIS

The Standard of Ur

In this investigation, you will analyze an intriguing artifact and additional information to answer questions about what life was like in ancient Sumer.

photo: Library of Congress

ACTIVITY TYPE: ROLE PLAY

A Day in the Life

In this activity, your class will work together to create various "living museum" scenes that depict daily life in the social classes of ancient Mesopotamia. You will use historical evidence as the basis for details in your group's scene.

© Discovery Education | www.DiscoveryEducation.com

PROJECTS AND ASSESSMENTS *(continued)*

photo: Discovery Education

ACTIVITY TYPE: EXPRESS YOUR OPINION

Women in Mesopotamia

How much power did women actually have in Mesopotamia? In this activity, you will gather information from various sources and then answer this question by writing a letter to a book editor or drawing a political cartoon that expresses your opinion and supports it with evidence from authoritative sources.

photo: Pixabay

ACTIVITY TYPE: DOCUMENT-BASED INVESTIGATION

Representing Our Values

What did the Mesopotamians value most? Nisaba, the narrator of the video segment "Religious Beliefs of the Ancient Sumerians," implies that Mesopotamians valued religion more than other aspects of life. In this investigation, you will decide for yourself after gathering information from primary source documents. Then, you will write a letter to Nisaba, supporting or opposing her stance, or you will create a documentary that shares your opinion about what the Mesopotamians valued the most.

Evaluate Activities

BRIEF-CONSTRUCTED RESPONSE (BCR)

Mesopotamian Society

EXTENDED-CONSTRUCTED RESPONSE (ECR)

Mesopotamian Society

UNIT 2: ANCIENT CIVILIZATIONS (C. 3500 TO 300 BCE)

Chapter 3: Mesopotamia

3.3 Mesopotamian Innovations and Contributions

photo: Getty Images

LESSON OVERVIEW

Lesson Objectives:

By the end of this lesson, you should be able to:

- Identify and analyze the impact of cultural and technical innovations of the Mesopotamians.
- Paraphrase portions of Hammurabi's Code and draw conclusions about the importance of codified laws to a society.

Key Vocabulary

Assyrian Empire, Assyrians, Babylonia, Code of Hammurabi, code of law, cuneiform, epic, Gilgamesh, Hammurabi, Nebuchadnezzar, rule of law, Sumerians

Lesson Essential Question:

How did Mesopotamian technological and cultural innovations influence future civilizations?

Name _____ **Date** _____

GRAPHIC ORGANIZER: Summary Frames

Use these Summary Frames to highlight the important events and ideas in The Epic of Gilgamesh. For supporting resources, go to Ancient Civilizations > Mesopotamia > Mesopotamian Innovations and Contributions > Explore > The Epic of Gilgamesh.

_____   _____   _____

_____   _____   _____

_____   _____   _____

_____   _____   _____

_____   _____   _____

Name _____ **Date** _____

GRAPHIC ORGANIZER: Main Idea Web

Use this Main Idea Web to records details about the Code of Hammurabi. For supporting resources, go to Ancient Civilizations > Mesopotamia > Mesopotamian Innovations and Contributions > Explore > The Law of the Land.

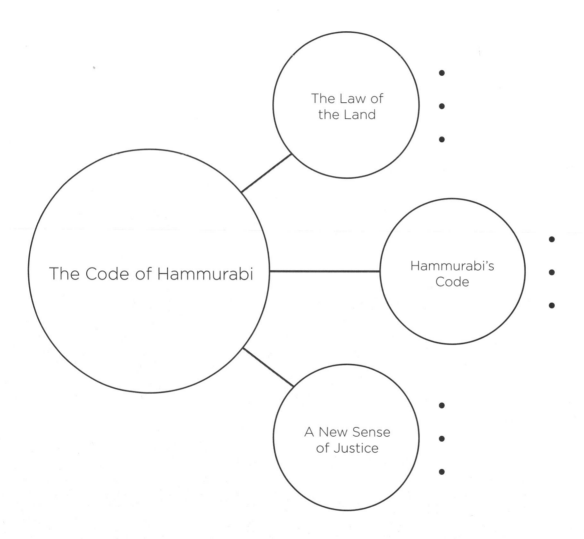

Name _____ Date _____

EXPLORE: FOCUS QUESTIONS

Using what you learned from the Core Interactive Text, answer each page's focus question:

The Development of Written Language
Why was the development of writing important?

_____

_____

_____

The Epic of Gilgamesh
What were Ancient Mesopotamian legends about?

_____

_____

_____

The Lessons of Gilgamesh
What does The Epic of Gilgamesh tell us about Sumerian culture?

_____

_____

_____

The Mesopotamian Calendar
How did the creation of a calendar improve agriculture?

_____

_____

_____

Advances in Technology
How did Mesopotamian technological innovations improve agriculture, trade, and transportation?

_____

_____

_____

The Law of the Land
How did Hammurabi's Code impact life in Mesopotamia?

_____

_____

_____

Name _____ **Date** _____

EXPLORE: FOCUS QUESTIONS *(continued)*

Hammurabi's Code
What laws were contained in Hammurabi's Code?

_____
_____
_____
_____

A New Sense of Justice
How did the Code of Hammurabi change the idea of justice?

_____
_____
_____

PROJECTS AND ASSESSMENTS

Explain Activities

ACTIVITY TYPE: MOVIE TRAILER

The Epic of Gilgamesh

The Epic of Gilgamesh is coming to a theater near you! You have been tasked with creating a movie trailer that will capture the nation's excitement. Use the frames to sketch out the trailer. The movie trailer should help the audience understand what the story is about and get them excited to see how the story unfolds in the movie. Consider including titles, narration, and music. Then, explain why you chose the scene, titles, narration, and music. Describe how your choices tell the audience about the story and about Mesopotamia.

ACTIVITY TYPE: ENCYCLOPEDIA ENTRY

Mesopotamian Innovations

In this activity, you will create an encyclopedia entry for one of the Mesopotamian innovations listed. Write an entry that clearly explains why the innovation was developed, what problems it helped to resolve, and how it influenced future civilizations.

ACTIVITY TYPE: SOCIAL STUDIES EXPLANATION

Mesopotamian Innovations and Contributions

In this Social Studies Explanation activity, you will use a template to assemble evidence from the sources you have explored. Then, you will write an answer to the Essential Question and defend your answer with supporting evidence.

Elaborate Activities

photo: Getty Images

INVESTIGATION TYPE: SOURCE ANALYSIS

Hammurabi's Code

Why are written laws for public behavior like Hammurabi's Code important for society? In this investigation, you will use the Source Analysis tool to examine a stone artifact that contains the legal rulings of Hammurabi.

PROJECTS AND ASSESSMENTS *(continued)*

photo: Library of Congress

ACTIVITY TYPE: YOU AS ARTIST

Modern Epic

In this creative writing exercise, you will choose an episode from The Epic of Gilgamesh and create a modern version of that episode.

photo: Pixabay

ACTIVITY TYPE: ROLE PLAY

On Trial: Hammurabi's Code

In this activity, you will write the story of a trial taking place in ancient Mesopotamia, under King Hammurabi's Code of Law.

photo: IRC

ACTIVITY TYPE: DOCUMENT-BASED INVESTIGATION

Laws Throughout the Ages

Imagine that you have traveled back in time to ancient Mesopotamia during Hammurabi's rule, but you have knowledge of modern-day laws. Write a letter to Hammurabi explaining how he influenced modern law and describe how laws have evolved since Hammurabi's time. Be sure to support your position using evidence from the primary sources.

Evaluate Activities

BRIEF-CONSTRUCTED RESPONSE (BCR)

Mesopotamian Innovations

EXTENDED-CONSTRUCTED RESPONSE (ECR)

Mesopotamian Innovations

photo: IRC

UNIT 2: ANCIENT CIVILIZATIONS (C. 3500 TO 300 BCE)

Chapter 4: Egypt

4.1 Geography of Egypt

LESSON OVERVIEW

Lesson Objectives:

By the end of this lesson, you should be able to:

- Locate ancient Egypt and its important cities and rivers on a historical and a modern map.
- Analyze how the geographical location of Egypt led to the development of a civilization.
- Explain the importance of trade to the ancient Egyptian economy and people.

Key Vocabulary

agriculture, command economy, delta, economy, Egypt, equator, Giza, Hatshepsut, intermediary period, irrigation, latitude, longitude, Lower Egypt, Mediterranean Sea, Memphis, Mesopotamia, Nile River, papyrus, silt, Thebes, trade, tradition-oriented economy, Upper Egypt

Lesson Essential Question:

How did Egypt's location influence its development?

FLASHCARDS

1 ▸ Land of the Nile

Egypt is located in northeastern Africa. Its ancient people created one of the world's earliest civilizations.

- The Nile is the most important feature of Egypt's geography, and it has played a major role in the country's history. It is surrounded by desert on either side.
- In both ancient and modern times, Egypt's population was centered along the Nile. Thebes, Memphis, and Giza were important cities in ancient Egypt. Important modern cities include Cairo, the capital; Alexandria; and Giza.
- As Egyptian civilization developed, two major kingdoms formed: Upper Egypt, which is along the Nile River; and Lower Egypt, which is in the Nile River delta.

Why Does It Matter?

Egypt's geography was the reason it developed into such an advanced civilization. Its major cities, and much of its population, were centered along the Nile. The river has made life in the region possible.

photo: Discovery Education

Almost all the cities of ancient and modern Egypt have developed along the Nile River.

2 ▸ Civilization Develops from Agriculture

Ancient Egyptians took advantage of the annual flooding of the Nile to develop a highly productive system of agriculture. This system helped to create a surplus of crops. This in turn helped lead to the creation of civilization in Egypt.

- Flood waters from Ethiopia annually flood the Nile with sediments that enrich the soil, especially the Nile River delta.
- Ancient Egyptians used irrigation techniques to help them grow a variety of crops, including grains, papyrus, and vegetables. They also raised domestic animals.
- Cooperation and organization were required to maintain the agricultural system. Governments grew as a result.
- The surplus of crops enabled some people to work in areas other than farming. Many people became craftsmen and artists, which helped to advance Egyptian civilization.

Why Does It Matter?

Egypt's location along the valley of the Nile made it an ideal location for the creation of a civilization. The Nile helped to provide a surplus of food, which led to the development of towns and cities, a variety of occupations, and the development of arts and crafts.

photo: Paul Fuqua

Every class of Egyptian played an important role in society.

FLASHCARDS *(continued)*

3 Trade Brings Great Wealth

The surplus of crops grown along the Nile River Valley provided the opportunity for trade. Egyptians traded their excess food for goods not available in their own kingdom and for luxury items.

- Egyptians exported crops such as wheat, barley, papyrus, and linen. They imported timber, copper, gold, and precious stones.
- Their trading partners were mainly other regions in Africa, such as Nubia and Punt, and parts of Southwest Asia.
- Imports were used to create luxury items for wealthy Egyptians.

Why Does It Matter?

The bounty of the Nile made Egypt very rich. Egyptians were able to use their surplus food to trade for goods they needed to survive, as well as for luxury items.

photo: Paul Fuqua

Trade was made possible by a surplus of crops grown along the Nile River.

Name _____ Date _____

GRAPHIC ORGANIZER: Cause/Effect Chart

Use this Cause/Effect Chart to identify how Egypt's geography and location (causes) have led to the growth of civilization (effects). For supporting resources, go to Ancient Civilizations > Egypt > Geography of Egypt > Explore > Egypt: Built Along a River.

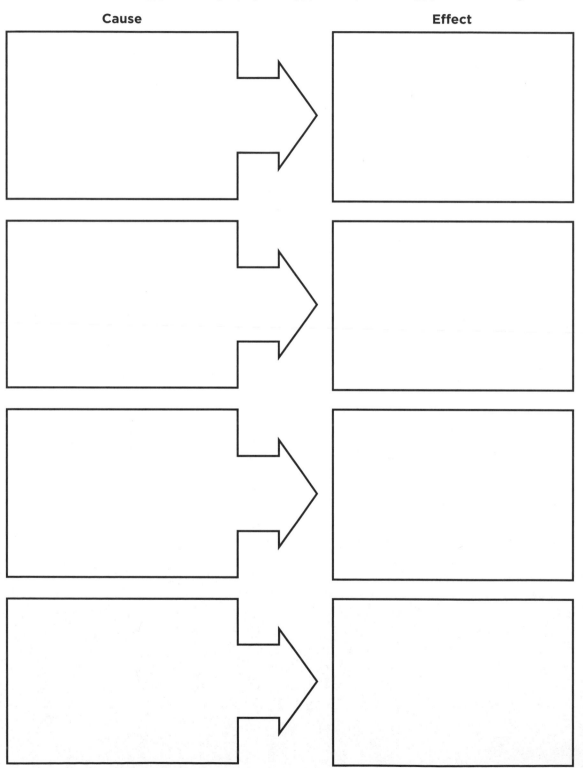

Cause   **Effect**

Name _____ Date _____

GRAPHIC ORGANIZER: Main Idea Web

Use this Main Idea Web to list three major geographic features of Egypt in the three circles. Then, identify three details about each geographic feature. For supporting resources, go to Ancient Civilizations > Egypt > Geography of Egypt > Explore > The Nile River.

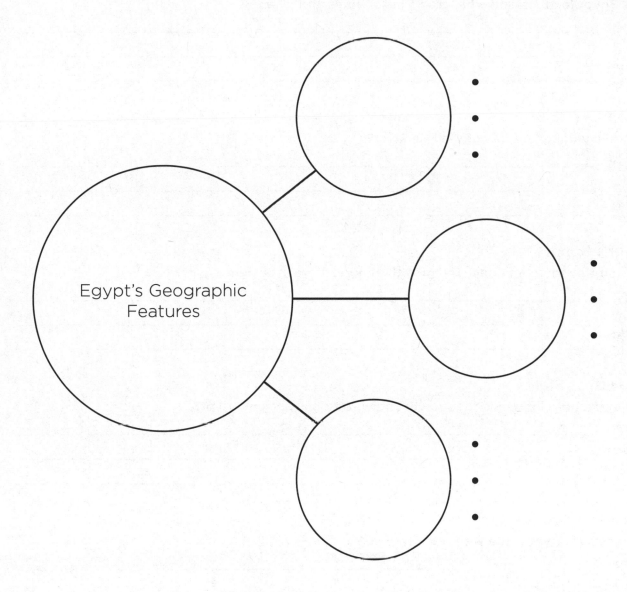

Egypt's Geographic Features

Name _____ Date _____

EXPLORE: FOCUS QUESTIONS

Using what you learned from the Core Interactive Text, answer each page's focus question:

Egypt: Built Along a River

Where is Egypt located, and what are its major cities and rivers?

_____
_____
_____

The Nile River

What are the unique features of the Nile River?

_____
_____
_____

The River's Bounty

How did the Nile River influence the growth of agriculture in ancient Egypt?

_____
_____
_____

The Growth of States

How did agriculture influence the growth of civilization in ancient Egypt?

_____
_____
_____

Egypt's Trade Economy

What goods did Egypt trade with other regions?

_____
_____
_____

Trade Brings Luxury

What was the impact of trade on Egyptian civilization?

_____
_____
_____

PROJECTS AND ASSESSMENTS

Explain Activities

ACTIVITY TYPE: DIAGRAM

Egypt and Mesopotamia

In this activity, you will use a Venn diagram to take notes on the similarities and differences in geography between the two civilizations.

ACTIVITY TYPE: VISUALIZATION

The Wealth of Egypt

In this activity, you will analyze the sequence of events that led to Egypt's becoming the world's wealthiest civilization by 1000 BCE. You will draw and write captions for illustrations that show the sequence of events.

ACTIVITY TYPE: SOCIAL STUDIES EXPLANATION

Geography of Egypt

In this Social Studies Explanation activity, you will use a template to assemble evidence from the sources you have explored. Then, you will write an answer to the Essential Question and defend your answer with supporting evidence.

Elaborate Activities

photo: Paul Fuqua

INVESTIGATION TYPE: MAP-GUIDED INQUIRY

Geography of Egypt

How did geography influence the development of a powerful civilization in ancient Egypt? How does ancient Egypt compare to modern Egypt on a map? Use the map tools in this activity to answer these and other questions.

ACTIVITY TYPE: SAY WHAT?

Hymn to the Nile

The ancient Egyptian city of Thebes is developing a new exhibit for its history museum. Sometime around 2100 BCE, an Egyptian priest wrote a hymn for a festival at Thebes celebrating the annual flood of the Nile River. Today, the Egyptian Museum directors want you to help them translate the hymn into modern language that students can understand. Read your portion of the hymn and translate it for modern times. Then, respond to the analysis questions.

photo: Library of Congress

PROJECTS AND ASSESSMENTS *(continued)*

photo: Paul Fuqua

ACTIVITY TYPE: CURRENT EVENTS CONNECTION

Rivers, Then and Now

In ancient times, civilizations relied upon rivers for life. Today, rivers still play an important role in many societies. After you analyze the ancient ode "Hymn to the Nile," use the resources provided to write your own ode to a modern-day river. Then, write an analysis comparing your river to the ancient Nile.

photo: Pixabay

ACTIVITY TYPE: DOCUMENT-BASED INVESTIGATION

Ancient Egypt's Far-Flung Trade

Write a letter to Professor Know-It-All in which you support or refute his assessment of ancient Egypt as a self-sufficient civilization. Use evidence from the sources to support your response.

Evaluate Activities

BRIEF-CONSTRUCTED RESPONSE (BCR)

Geography of Egypt

EXTENDED-CONSTRUCTED RESPONSE (ECR)

Geography of Egypt

photo: Paul Fuqua

UNIT 2: ANCIENT CIVILIZATIONS (C. 3500 TO 300 BCE)

Chapter 4: Egypt
4.2 Egyptian Society

LESSON OVERVIEW

Lesson Objectives:

By the end of this lesson, you should be able to:

- Explain the concept of a dynasty and identify the important dynasties in ancient Egypt.
- Analyze the roles of the following in ancient Egypt: pharaoh, peasants, and enslaved people.
- Explain the religious practices of ancient Egyptians.

Key Vocabulary

civilization, Cleopatra VII, dynasty, Egyptians, Giza, glyph, Hatshepsut, hieroglyphics, Khufu, Kush, Memphis, Menes, Middle Kingdom, New Kingdom, Nile River, Old Kingdom, papyrus, peasant, pharaoh, polytheism, pyramid, Ramses II, social class, social pyramid, Takarka, Thebes, Thutmose III, Tutankhamen, Valley of Kings

Lesson Essential Question:

What effects did power and social class have on the lives of ancient Egyptians?

FLASHCARDS

1 Egyptian Dynasties

The Kingdoms of Upper and Lower Egypt united around 3100 BCE. For most of the next 3,000 years, this land was ruled by powerful kings called pharaohs.

- Historians divide ancient Egypt into three distinct time periods: the Old Kingdom, the Middle Kingdom, and the New Kingdom. During these time periods, pharaohs ruled the empire and passed their power down from one generation to another through ruling dynasties.
- Pharaohs waged wars to expand their empires and built elaborate temples and tombs that still stand throughout Egypt today.
- Historians have learned about pharaohs such as Khufu, Hatshepsut, Thutmose III, and Ramses II from the artifacts left behind in their tombs and temples.

Why Does It Matter?

Egypt was one of the largest and most influential kingdoms in the ancient world. Pharaohs had immense power over the people of Egypt.

photo: Paul Fuqua
This statue of Ramses II is from one of the many temples he built during his reign.

2 Calling Rank

Ancient Egyptians created a social pyramid that ranked members of society based on their status.

- The ancient Egyptians believed that pharaohs were gods.
- A small group of government officials and priests served the pharaohs.
- Skilled workers, such as scribes and craftsmen, created written works and artifacts, many of which survive today.
- The majority of Egyptians were farmers who farmed the land. Enslaved people had the lowest status in ancient Egypt.

Why Does It Matter?

Every class in the social structure contributed to Egyptian society, and all classes supported the power of the pharaoh. The pharaoh's decisions about war, building projects, and succession could affect the lives of every Egyptian.

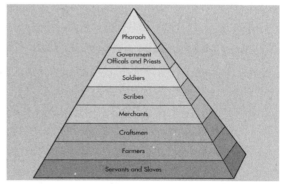

photo: Discovery Education
Every class of Egyptian played an important role in society.

FLASHCARDS *(continued)*

3 ▸ Egyptian Religion

Ancient Egyptians were polytheists who believed in many gods. They also believed that the dead lived on in the afterlife.

- **Osiris, Isis, Horus, and Seth were among the chief gods of Egypt. The pharaoh was considered an embodiment of Horus on Earth.**

- **To prepare for the afterlife, pharaohs ordered their subjects to build elaborate tombs full of fine objects.**

- **After death, a pharaoh's body was carefully mummified, or preserved, by priests before being placed in a tomb.**

Why Does It Matter?

The ancient Egyptians' focus on the afterlife is one of the reasons that their culture has been so well preserved. Builders went to enormous lengths to provide secure buildings to house the pharaohs' bodies after death. Artists and scribes created works to record the glorious past of the pharaohs. Tomb art, including hieroglyphics, gives historians clues about what happened in ancient Egypt.

photo: Pixabay

The Book of the Dead was a collection of religious texts designed to guide the deceased to eternal life.

Name _____ Date _____

GRAPHIC ORGANIZER: Vocabulary Chart

Use this Vocabulary Chart to define the word *dynasty*. For supporting resources, go to Ancient Civilizations > Egypt > Egyptian Society > Explore > Pharaohs Unify Egypt.

DEFINITION:

Personal:

Dictionary:

EXAMPLES (Drawn or Written):

TERM:
dynasty

SENTENCES:
Teacher/Book:

Personal:

RELATED:

WORD PARTS:

Outside of School (Who Would Use the Word? How Would He or She Use It?):

Name _____ **Date** _____

GRAPHIC ORGANIZER: Timeline

Use this Timeline to chart information on Egypt's kingdoms. For supporting resources, go to Ancient Civilizations > Egypt > Egyptian Society > Explore > Egypt's Kingdoms.

3100 BCE   1075 BCE

Name _____ **Date** _____

 GRAPHIC ORGANIZER: Comparison Chart

Use this Comparison Chart to record information about each group in ancient Egyptian society. For supporting resources, go to Ancient Civilizations > Egypt > Egyptian Society > Explore > The Social Structure of Ancient Egypt.

Group	Roles	Responsibilities
Pharoah		
Government Officials		
Priests		
Soldiers		
Scribes		

Name _____ **Date** _____

GRAPHIC ORGANIZER: Main Idea Web

Use this Main Idea Web to connect details about Egyptian religion. For supporting resources, go to Ancient Civilizations > Egypt > Egyptian Society > Explore > Gods and Goddesses of Ancient Egypt.

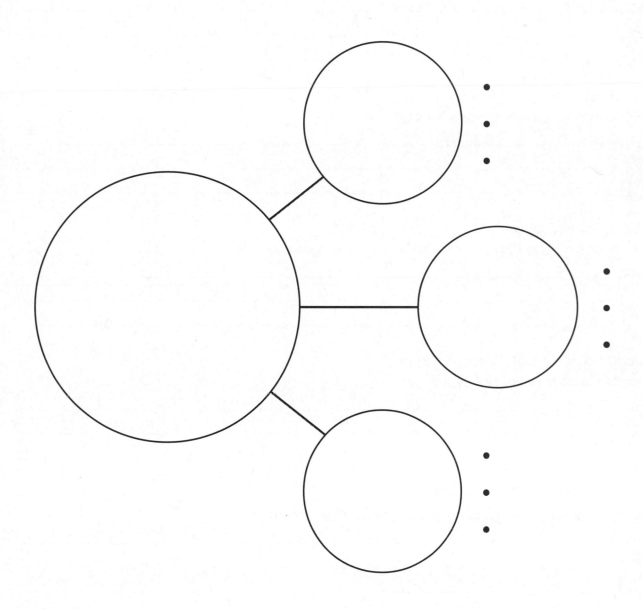

Name _____ Date _____

EXPLORE: FOCUS QUESTIONS

Using what you learned from the Core Interactive Text, answer each page's focus question:

Pharaohs Unify Egypt

What is a dynasty? How did ancient Egyptians choose rulers?

_____
_____
_____
_____

Egypt's Kingdoms

How do historians organize Egypt's history?

_____
_____
_____
_____

Great Leaders of Egypt

How did Egypt's most powerful rulers leave their marks on history?

_____
_____
_____
_____

The Social Structure of Ancient Egypt

What was life like for ordinary Egyptians?

_____
_____
_____
_____

Government Officials and Priests

How did the pharaoh maintain control over such a large empire?

_____
_____
_____
_____

Name _____ Date _____

EXPLORE: FOCUS QUESTIONS *(continued)*

Soldiers and Scribes
How did the Egyptian empire continue to grow and thrive?

_____

_____

_____

Merchants and Craftsmen
How did the pharaohs get so many artifacts for their temples and tombs?

_____

_____

_____

Farmers and Enslaved People
Who supplied Egypt's food and built the pyramids?

_____

_____

_____

Gods and Goddesses of Ancient Egypt
How did religion influence Egyptian society?

_____

_____

_____

Life After Death
Why were tombs so important to ancient Egyptians?

_____

_____

_____

PROJECTS AND ASSESSMENTS

Explain Activities

ACTIVITY TYPE: DIAGRAM

Egyptian Society

Use at least eight words from the word bank to create a graphic answer to the Essential Question. You may add any other words or symbols, but you must use all of the starred words. Summarize your map at the bottom and be prepared to present your thinking.

ACTIVITY TYPE: QUICK WRITE

Egyptian Society

In this Quick Write, you will take the perspective of an Egyptian pharaoh reflecting on the significance of his or her accomplishments.

ACTIVITY TYPE: SOCIAL STUDIES EXPLANATION

Egyptian Society

In this Social Studies Explanation activity, you will use a template to assemble evidence from the sources you have explored. Then, you will write an answer to the Essential Question and defend your answer with supporting evidence.

Elaborate Activities

photo: Getty Images

INVESTIGATION TYPE: SOURCE ANALYSIS

Egyptian Scribe

What were some of the sources of power and social class in ancient Egypt? Your mission is to study the many contributions that scribes made to Egyptian society and identify the reasons why literacy was so important to their civilization.

photo: Paul Fuqua

ACTIVITY TYPE: DOCUMENT-BASED INVESTIGATION

Daily Life in Ancient Egypt

What were the roles of a government official, soldier, scribe, and farmer in ancient Egypt? Which of these groups was most important to Egyptian society? In this activity, you will create a museum exhibit or write a brief essay arguing why one group was more important to Egyptian society than the others.

PROJECTS AND ASSESSMENTS *(continued)*

photo: Associated Press

ACTIVITY TYPE: CURRENT EVENTS CONNECTION

Dynasties: Then and Now

In this activity, you will be comparing the pharaoh to two modern dynasties to determine which has more in common with the ancient rulers of Egypt. Then, you will express your opinion in an article in response to the following question: Was the pharaoh more like the modern British royal family or the Kim dynasty in North Korea?

photo: Pixabay

ACTIVITY: SAY WHAT?

Precepts of Ptah-Hotep

The president wants to create a book of advice to young students to inspire them to grow into great leaders. Your class has been asked to review advice given to young leaders throughout ancient history and translate it for a modern audience as part of this project.

Evaluate Activities

BRIEF-CONSTRUCTED RESPONSE (BCR)

Egyptian Society

EXTENDED-CONSTRUCTED RESPONSE (ECR)

Egyptian Society

UNIT 2: ANCIENT CIVILIZATIONS (C. 3500 TO 300 BCE)

Chapter 4: Egypt

4.3 Egyptian Innovations and Contributions

LESSON OVERVIEW

Lesson Objective:

By the end of this lesson, you should be able to:

- **Connect the technological and cultural innovations of Egyptian civilization to the development of its neighbors and future civilizations.**

Lesson Essential Question:

How did the innovations of ancient Egypt impact its neighbors and future civilizations?

Key Vocabulary

anatomy, barter, command economy, cubit, cultural diffusion, deity, Hatshepsut, hieroglyphics, kohl, logogram, Lower Egypt, Mediterranean Sea, mummy, mural, papyrus, pharaoh, phonograms, Rosetta Stone, scribe, stylus, Thutmose III, Tutankhamen, Upper Egypt

FLASHCARDS

1 Egyptian Innovations

The Egyptians were very innovative. They made many cultural and technological advancements, which improved their quality of life and impacted their neighbors and future generations.

- King Tutankhamen's tomb was filled with well-made furniture, jewelry, clothing, and personal items.
- They developed hieroglyphics, a kind of writing, and the first paper.
- They standardized weights and measures so they could construct great buildings and conduct trade throughout the region.
- Their doctors were the first to study medicine in a careful way. They learned how to treat many illnesses and injuries. Some physicians even performed surgery.
- Their artists and craftspeople created sophisticated paintings and sculptures.

Why Does It Matter?

Technological and cultural advances meant Egyptians had a high standard of living. Egyptians could sell or trade their innovations to other societies, which made Egypt a powerful and influential nation. Many societies adopted and adapted the cultural and technological innovations of the Egyptians. Some of their innovations are still used today.

photo: Library of Congress

This engraving is from an Egyptian stele.

2 Egyptian Trading

Egyptian rulers and merchants used trade routes to buy and sell goods. Their caravans carried many things besides merchandise.

- The Egyptians taught others the skills of writing, measuring, and building.
- Doctors shared their knowledge about medicine.
- Artists and sculptors sold their creations to important and wealthy people in other countries.
- Trade routes used by the Egyptians sometimes crossed other routes. Those went to places even farther away, like Asia and India.

Why Does It Matter?

Trading meant that Egyptian innovations and technology were used around the world. People in other countries were able to improve their lives. They adapted the Egyptian products to fit their needs. They added to the knowledge they learned from the Egyptians and invented new technology. Those new innovations traveled to even more places and changed even more lives.

photo: Paul Fuqua

Camels laden with goods from gold to flax crossed the desert of trade routes throughout Egypt, North Africa, the Mediterranean coastlines, and farther to India and Asia.

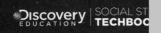
Name _____ Date _____

GRAPHIC ORGANIZER: GREASES Chart

Use this GREASES chart to explore what Tutankhamen's tomb can show us about Egyptian society. For supporting resources, go to Ancient Civilizations > Egypt > Egyptian Innovations and Contributions > Explore > King Tutankhamen's Tomb.

TOPIC: Tutankhamen and Egypt

	What I See	My Conclusions
Government		
Religion		
Economic		
Art & Architecture		
Science & Technology		
Environment		
Social & Cultural Values		

Name _____ Date _____

GRAPHIC ORGANIZER: Problem/Solution Chart

Complete this Problem/Solution Chart. For supporting resources, go to Ancient Civilizations > Egypt > Egyptian Innovations and Contributions > Explore > The Arts and Crafts of Ancient Egypt.

Problem	**Solution**
Medicinal Herbs and Plants	Medicinal Herbs and Plants
Pyramids	Pyramids
Hieroglyphics	Hieroglyphics

Name _____ **Date** _____

GRAPHIC ORGANIZER: Problem/Solution Chart *(continued)*

Problem   **Solution**

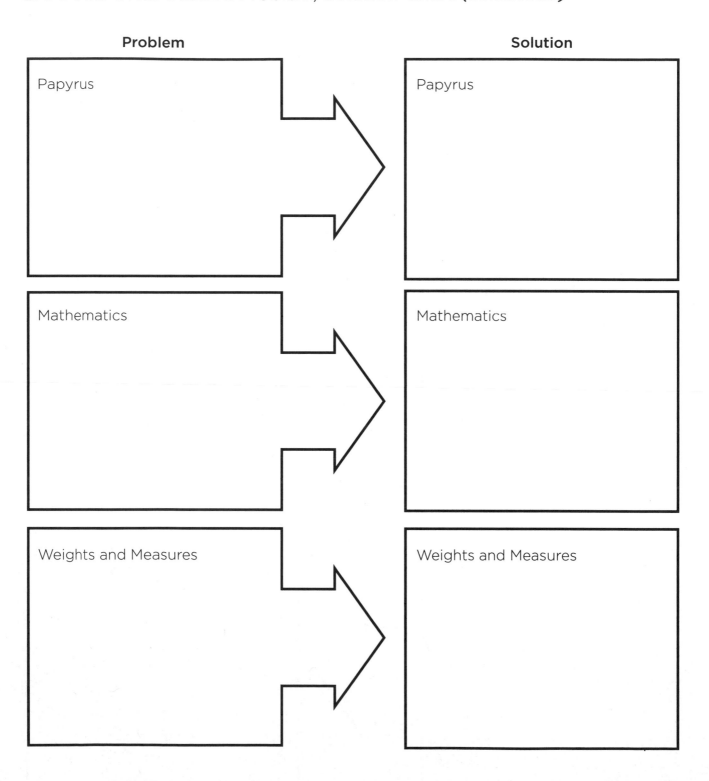

Papyrus   Papyrus

Mathematics   Mathematics

Weights and Measures   Weights and Measures

Name _____ Date _____

EXPLORE: FOCUS QUESTIONS

Using what you learned from the Core Interactive Text, answer each page's focus question:

King Tutankhamen's Tomb

What do the contents of King Tutankhamen's tomb tell us about life in ancient Egypt?

_____

_____

_____

The Arts and Crafts of Ancient Egypt

What was the importance of ancient Egyptian art?

_____

_____

_____

Egyptian Mythology

How did the religion and mythology of Ancient Egypt influence other cultures?

_____

_____

_____

Medical Discoveries

What did the Egyptians know about medicine?

_____

_____

_____

The Architecture of the Pyramids

How did the pyramids influence architecture?

_____

_____

_____

Name _____ **Date** _____

EXPLORE: FOCUS QUESTIONS *(continued)*

Reading and Writing in Ancient Egypt

Which Egyptian innovations changed the way people communicate?

_____
_____
_____
_____

The Invention of Paper

How did Egyptians preserve their written records?

_____
_____
_____
_____

Mathematics

What did the Egyptians know about mathematics?

_____
_____
_____
_____

How Much and How Big

Why did Egyptians develop a standard system of weights and measures?

_____
_____
_____
_____

Trade Networks

How did Egyptian innovations spread throughout the world?

_____
_____
_____

PROJECTS AND ASSESSMENTS

Explain Activities

ACTIVITY TYPE: ADVERTISEMENT

Egyptian Innovations and Contributions

In this activity, you will create an advertisement for an ancient Egyptian innovation or contribution. Before creating the advertisement, use the graphic organizer to respond to questions.

ACTIVITY TYPE: QUICK WRITE

Egyptian Innovations and Contributions

Which ancient innovation is the most important to the modern world, and why? In this Quick Write activity, you will write a paragraph explaining which of the ancient Egyptian innovations you learned about is the most important to people today and explain why.

ACTIVITY TYPE: SOCIAL STUDIES EXPLANATION

Egyptian Innovations and Contributions

In this Social Studies Explanation activity, you will use a template to assemble evidence from the sources you have explored. Then, you will write an answer to the Essential Question and defend your answer with supporting evidence.

Elaborate Activities

photo. Getty Images

INVESTIGATION TYPE: SOURCE ANALYSIS

Rosetta Stone

How did the discovery of the Rosetta Stone help archaeologists learn about the culture and technology of ancient Egypt? In this investigation, you will analyze the Rosetta Stone and explain how scholars decoded the Egyptian hieroglyphics that teach us about this ancient civilization.

PROJECTS AND ASSESSMENTS *(continued)*

photo: Paul Fuqua

ACTIVITY TYPE: PITCH YOUR IDEA

Bid for Pyramid Construction

How did the ancient Egyptians construct the massive pyramids without the help of modern technology? In this activity, imagine that you own a construction company in ancient Egypt. Prepare a presentation to convince the pharaoh that your company should build the newest pyramid.

photo: Library of Congress

ACTIVITY TYPE: CURRENT EVENTS CONNECTION

How Do Countries Get Rich?

In this activity, you will write an interview between you and an ancient Egyptian citizen and another interview between you and a modern-day Chinese citizen, in which you ask: How did your country become rich?

photo: Library of Congress

ACTIVITY TYPE: DOCUMENT-BASED INVESTIGATION

Writing's Impact on Egypt

In this activity, imagine you are an Egyptologist (an archeologist who specializes in the study of ancient Egypt). You have been asked to be a guest lecturer at a conference about ancient civilizations. Prepare a presentation about the impact of writing on ancient Egyptian society.

Evaluate Activities

BRIEF-CONSTRUCTED RESPONSE (BCR)

Egyptian Innovations and Contributions

EXTENDED-CONSTRUCTED RESPONSE (ECR)

Egyptian Innovations and Contributions

photo: Getty Images

UNIT 2: ANCIENT CIVILIZATIONS (C. 3500 TO 300 BCE)

Chapter 5: Kush and Phoenicia

5.1 Kush Geography and Society

LESSON OVERVIEW

Lesson Objectives:

By the end of this lesson, you should be able to:

- Locate ancient Kush and its important cities and rIvers on both historical and modern maps.
- Analyze the importance of the location of Kush, including its natural resources and its proximity to Egypt.
- Connect the technological and cultural innovations of Kush civilization to the development of its neighbors and future civilizations.

Key Vocabulary

Assyrian Empire, cultural diffusion, Egypt, Ethiopia, Kush, Kush's conquest of Egypt, Nile River, Nubia, pharaoh, Red Sea

Lesson Essential Question:

How did trade help change and spread ancient Kush culture?

FLASHCARDS

1 The Kingdom of Kush

Kush was an enormous kingdom that occupied important territory in the ancient world.

- Kush was located on the Nile River south of Egypt.
- Much of its eastern boundary was the Red Sea.
- It was also known as Nubia, which means "Land of Gold," because it had vast deposits of the metal.
- Its major cities were Kerma, Napata, and Meroe.
- The Kingdom of Kush included parts of modern Sudan, Egypt, and Ethiopia.

Why Does It Matter?

The size and location of Kush made it a major political and economic force in the ancient world.

photo: Discovery Education
Kush was located along the Nile River, south of Egypt.

2 Kush's Location and Resources

The kingdom's proximity to Egypt helped make Kush a regional power.

- Kush controlled trade between Egypt and central Africa.
- Its frequent and close contact with Egypt resulted in the adoption and adaptation of many Egyptian ideas and customs.
- It engaged in many battles with Egypt for control of the region and for the other kingdom's wealth.
- The Kush King Piye conquered all of Egypt.
- When Piye took control of all of Egypt, the combined kingdoms of Kush and Egypt stretched from the Nile Delta to the modern-day city of Khartoum.

Why Does It Matter?

Each kingdom wanted to control the wealth of the entire region. The trade routes were a major source of income, power, and influence. The Egyptian customs and technology were adopted and adapted by the Kushites. They saw the value in learning to write, worshipped Egyptian gods, and dressed in Egyptian fashions.

photo: Getty Images
Warriors from Kush often fought alongside Egyptian troops.

FLASHCARDS *(continued)*

3 ### Kush Influence

Kush had advantages of location and resources that brought it wealth and allowed it to influence other cultures.

- **It controlled traffic on the Nile River and a major port on the Red Sea.**
- **Trade from the Mediterranean, Egypt, the Middle East, and Sub-Saharan Africa all passed through Kush.**
- **Travelers carried their customs, language, foods, religions, and fashions with them.**
- **Kush workmen learned how to smelt iron ore and make iron tools and weapons.**

Why Does It Matter?

As a hub for trading routes from throughout the known world, Kush became a transfer point for materials, goods, ideas, technology, and innovation.

photo: Bigstock

Researchers are still learning about the wealth and knowledge of Kush.

Name _____ **Date** _____

GRAPHIC ORGANIZER: Main Idea Web

Use this Main Idea Web to list characteristics of ancient Kush's location, physical geography, and natural resources. For supporting resources, go to Ancient Civilizations > Kush and Phoenicia > Kush Geography and Society > Explore > The Kingdom of Kush— Then and Now.

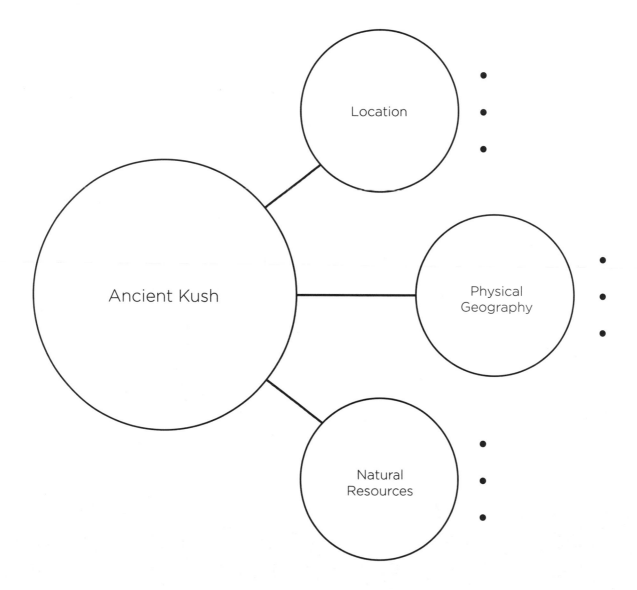

© Discovery Education | www.DiscoveryEducation.com

Discovery | SOCIAL STUDIES
EDUCATION | **TECHBOOK**

Name _____ Date _____

GRAPHIC ORGANIZER: Cause/Event/Effect Chart 1

Use this Cause/Event/Effect Chart to record how events in Egypt affected ancient Kush society. For supporting resources, go to Ancient Civilizations > Kush and Phoenicia > Kush Geography and Society > Explore > Cultural Connections.

Cause	Event	Effect

Name _____   **Date** _____

GRAPHIC ORGANIZER: Cause/Event/Effect Chart 2

Use this Cause/Event/Effect Chart to record how events in ancient Kush influenced its neighbors. For supporting resources, go to Ancient Civilizations > Kush and Phoenicia > Kush Geography and Society > Explore > Crossroads of Commerce and Ideas.

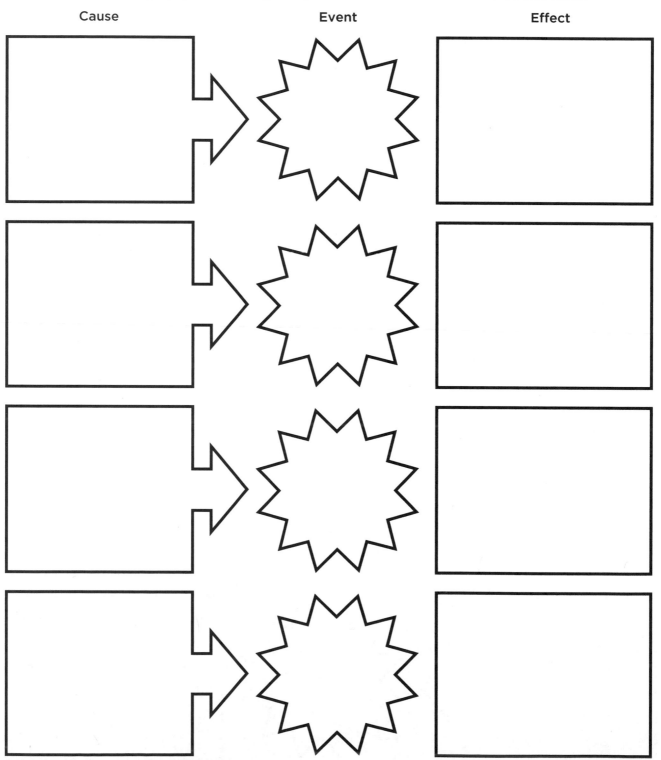

Cause   Event   Effect

Name _____ Date _____

EXPLORE: FOCUS QUESTIONS

Using what you learned from the Core Interactive Text, answer each page's focus question:

The Kingdom of Kush—Then and Now
Where was ancient Kush?

_____

_____

_____

Resources and Location
How did Kush gain power and influence?

_____

_____

_____

Cultural Connections
How did Egypt influence Kush?

_____

_____

_____

Conquered and Conquering
How well did Kush and Egypt get along?

_____

_____

_____

Crossroads of Commerce and Ideas
How did Kush influence its neighbors?

_____

_____

_____

PROJECTS AND ASSESSMENTS

Explain Activities

ACTIVITY TYPE: DIAGRAM

Kush: Geography and Society

Use at least 10 words from the word bank to create a graphic answer to the Essential Question. You may add any other words or symbols, but you must use all of the starred words. Summarize your map at the bottom and be prepared to present your thinking.

ACTIVITY TYPE: YOU AS JOURNALIST

Kush Trading Trip

In this activity, you will write a travel article describing your trading trip to Kush. First, complete the graphic organizer to answer questions about the trip. Then, use your notes in the organizer to write a news article that answers each of the questions from the graphic organizer.

ACTIVITY TYPE: SOCIAL STUDIES EXPLANATION

Kush Geography and Society

In this Social Studies Explanation activity, you will use a template to assemble evidence from the sources you have explored. Then, you will write an answer to the Essential Question and defend your answer with supporting evidence.

Elaborate Activities

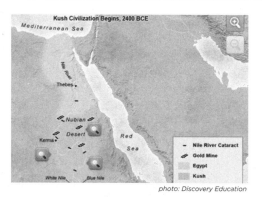

photo: Discovery Education

INVESTIGATION TYPE: TIMELINE MAP

The Splendor of Ancient Kush

What did ancient Kush culture gain from other civilizations? How were other civilizations influenced by ancient Kush culture? In this investigation, you will use the Timeline Map interactive tool to analyze how the culture of ancient Kush was changed by trade.

PROJECTS AND ASSESSMENTS *(continued)*

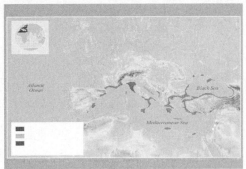

photo: Discovery Education

ACTIVITY TYPE: PITCH YOUR IDEA

Ancient Geography

Imagine you are the adviser to a wealthy queen in Southwest Asia around 1000 BCE. Your city has been destroyed by an earthquake, and all of your citizens believe your current location is cursed. All of the people want to start over in a new location, but where? In this activity, you will pitch a proposal to the queen, identifying and describing the best location for your relocated civilization.

photo: From The New York Public Library

ACTIVITY TYPE: EXPRESS YOUR OPINION

Should We Continue to Trade?

In this activity, you will create a political cartoon or write an op-ed article from the perspective of an ancient Nubian explaining your position on whether or not Kush should continue to trade with the neighboring Egyptians. Examine the sources that describe Kush's relationship with ancient Egypt to determine whether the relationship is a beneficial or harmful one.

photo: Paul Fuqua

ACTIVITY TYPE: DOCUMENT-BASED INVESTIGATION

Kush: An Independent Culture?

Use the artifacts in this investigation to develop a position on the topic of whether Kush culture was independent of Egyptian culture. Then, prepare a presentation for an archaeological conference in which you defend your position.

Evaluate Activities

BRIEF-CONSTRUCTED RESPONSE (BCR)

Kush Geography and Society

EXTENDED-CONSTRUCTED RESPONSE (ECR)

Kush Geography and Society

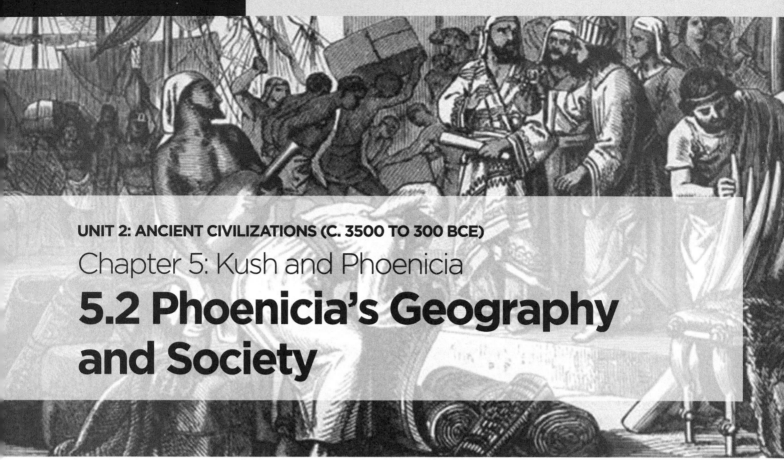

UNIT 2: ANCIENT CIVILIZATIONS (C. 3500 TO 300 BCE)

Chapter 5: Kush and Phoenicia

5.2 Phoenicia's Geography and Society

LESSON OVERVIEW

Lesson Objectives:

By the end of this lesson, you should be able to:

- Explain the connection between the location of Phoenicia and its importance to sea-based trading.

- Analyze the influence of neighboring cultures on political organization and culture in Phoenicia.

- Analyze the advantages of a simple, shared writing system for the Phoenicians.

Key Vocabulary

Carthage, city-state, colony, cultural diffusion, Europe, Lebanon, Mediterranean Sea, overland trade, Phoenicia, Phoenicians, port cities, self-government, trade, tribute

Lesson Essential Question:

In what ways did the sea shape Phoenician society and its impact on the outside world?

FLASHCARDS

1 ▸ A Great Trading Empire

Phoenicia was a major trading power in the Mediterranean region. Over time, the Phoenicians expanded their empire by establishing colonies.

- Phoenicia was located along the eastern coast of the Mediterranean Sea. Its major port cities included Tyre and Sidon.
- The Phoenicians mainly traded cedar wood, metal goods, pottery, glass, animal skins, and dyed cloth.
- Phoenicia established many colonies along the North African coast and throughout the Mediterranean. The most powerful Phoenician colony was Carthage.
- The Phoenicians controlled trade throughout the Mediterranean for over 300 years.

Why Does It Matter?

The Phoenicians relied upon the sea for their economic survival. Through their use of the sea, they established a strong and expansive trade network. Some of the colonies that the Phoenicians established would become historically important cities and civilizations.

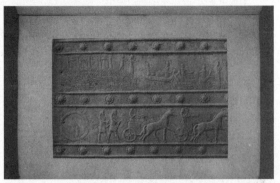

photo: The New York Public Library
The Phoenicians established a vast trading empire. Trade drove much of their daily lives and culture.

2 ▸ Phoenician Culture

The interaction among the Phoenician, Greek, Egyptian, and Mesopotamian peoples greatly influenced Phoenician culture. Through cultural diffusion, the Phoenicians adopted many aspects of Greek and Mesopotamian culture.

- Phoenicia was often under the occupation of other cultures such as Mesopotamia or Egypt.
- Phoenicia was organized into independent city-states.
- The Phoenicians adopted many aspects of culture from the Mesopotamians.
- The Phoenician culture was very dependent upon the sea.

Why Does It Matter?

The peoples of the Mediterranean world became more alike through the adoption and adaption of one another's cultures.

photo: Discovery Education
The Phoenicians adopted many aspects of their culture from their Mesopotamian neighbors.

FLASHCARDS *(continued)*

3 ▸ The Phoenician Alphabet

The Phoenician writing system, which was simpler and more efficient than those of neighboring civilizations, spread throughout the Mediterranean world.

- **The Phoenician alphabet was based on 22 consonant sound-symbols, rather than word-symbols.**
- **The alphabet helped Phoenicians conduct trade and keep records.**
- **Later civilizations adopted and adapted the Phoenician script.**

Why Does It Matter?

The Phoenician alphabet was a simplified system of writing. This simplified system increased literacy. The creation of the Phoenician alphabet led to the creation of the alphabet that is used in many parts of the modern world.

Phoenican Letter	Latin Letter
⟨	A
◁	B
⅂	C
◁	D

photo: Discovery Education
The Phoenicians developed one of the earliest alphabets.

Name _____ **Date** _____

GRAPHIC ORGANIZER: Main Idea Web

Use this Main Idea Web to record details about Phoenicia's physical location, geographic features, and the benefits or disadvantages of its proximity to the sea. For supporting resources, go to Ancient Civilizations > Kush and Phoenicia > Phoenicia's Geography and Society > Explore > Phoenicia: Coastal Civilization.

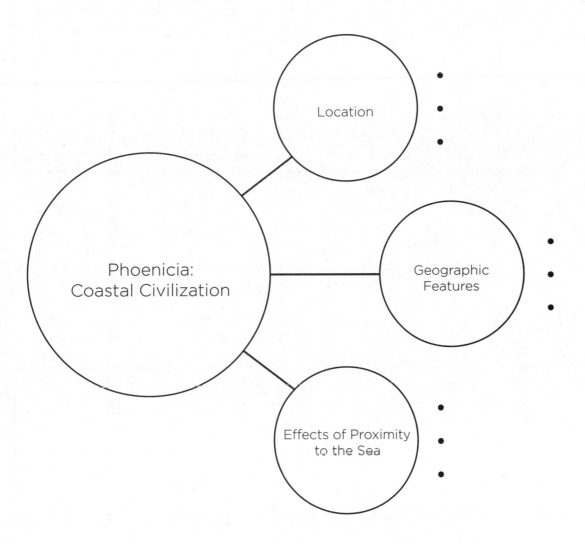

SOCIAL STUDIES
TECHBOOK

Name _____ **Date** _____

GRAPHIC ORGANIZER: Summary Frames

Use these Summary Frames to illustrate four to six events that helped the Phoenicians become the dominant trade force in the Mediterranean. For supporting resources, go to Ancient Civilizations > Kush and Phoenicia > Phoenicia's Geography and Society > Explore > The "Red People" Begin to Trade.

Name _____ Date _____

GRAPHIC ORGANIZER: GREASES Chart

Use this GREASES Chart to record information about Phoenicia's government, religion, economy, art and architecture, science and technology, environment, and social and cultural values. For supporting resources, go to Ancient Civilizations > Kush and Phoenicia > Phoenicia's Geography and Society > Explore > Phoenician Culture and Government.

	What I See	My Conclusions
Government		
Religion		
Economic		
Art & Architecture		
Science & Technology		
Environment		
Social & Cultural Values		

Name _____ Date _____

EXPLORE: FOCUS QUESTIONS

Using what you learned from the Core Interactive Text, answer each page's focus question:

Phoenicia: Coastal Civilization

Where was Phoenicia?

_____
_____
_____
_____

The "Red People" Begin to Trade

How did the Phoenicians come to dominate trade in the Mediterranean?

_____
_____
_____
_____

Phoenician Culture and Government

Who ruled Phoenicia?

_____
_____
_____
_____

Egyptian and Mesopotamian Influence

What societies had an impact on Phoenician culture?

_____
_____
_____
_____

Name _____   Date _____

EXPLORE: FOCUS QUESTIONS

Using what you learned from the Core Interactive Text, answer each page's focus question:

The Written Word

How did the Phoenicians impact other cultures?

_____

_____

_____

The Development of the Modern Alphabet

How did the Phoenician alphabet lead to the modern-day alphabet?

_____

_____

_____

PROJECTS AND ASSESSMENTS

Explain Activities

ACTIVITY TYPE: ADVERTISEMENT

Buying Phoenician Innovations

In this activity, you will create an advertisement for an ancient Phoenician innovation or contribution.

ACTIVITY TYPE: DIAGRAM

Ancient Civilizations

In this activity, you will use a comparison chart to compare the government and economic systems, art and architecture, and innovations of three civilizations: Phoenicia, Mesopotamia, and Egypt.

ACTIVITY TYPE: SOCIAL STUDIES EXPLANATION

Phoenicia's Geography and Society

In this Social Studies Explanation activity, you will use a template to assemble evidence from the sources you have explored. Then, you will write an answer to the Essential Question and defend your answer with supporting evidence.

Elaborate Activities

photo: Discovery Education

ACTIVITY TYPE: CURRENT EVENTS CONNECTION

Ancient and Modern Trade

In this activity, you will use the map to learn how trade has evolved since the time of the Phoenicians.

photo: The New York Public Library

ACTIVITY TYPE: ROLE PLAY

Life as a Phoenician Sailor

In this activity, you will write a series of diary entries describing the experiences of a Phoenician sailor in different port cities.

PROJECTS AND ASSESSMENTS *(continued)*

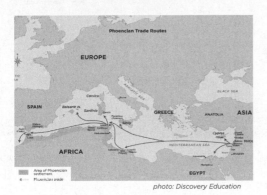

photo: Discovery Education

ACTIVITY TYPE: STUDENT SLEUTH

Phoenician Trade Routes

In this activity, you will investigate the Phoenicians' trade routes and then practice determining distances and using cardinal and intermediate directions.

Evaluate Activities

BRIEF-CONSTRUCTED RESPONSE (BCR)

Phoenicia's Geography and Society

EXTENDED-CONSTRUCTED RESPONSE (ECR)

Phoenicia's Geography and Society

photo: Getty Images

UNIT 3: REGIONAL CIVILIZATIONS | 2500 BCE TO 1054 CE

Chapter 6: Ancient India

6.1 Geography of India

LESSON OVERVIEW

Lesson Objectives:

By the end of this lesson, you should be able to:

- **Locate ancient India and explain the importance of physical geography to the development of Indian civilizations.**

Lesson Essential Question:

How did physical geography shape Indian civilization?

Key Vocabulary

Agra, alluvial plain, Arabian Sea, citadel, climate, Ganges River, Ganges Valley, Harappa, Himalayas, India, Indian Subcontinent, Indus Plain, Indus River, landform, Mohenjo-daro, monsoon, Mount Everest, mountain range, Sarasvati River, South Asia, subcontinent, surplus, tradition-oriented economy

Name _____ **Date** _____

GRAPHIC ORGANIZER: GREASES Chart

Use this GREASES Chart to record information about the government, religion, economics, art and architecture, science and technology, environment, and social and cultural values of ancient India. For supporting resources, go to Regional Civilizations > Ancient India > Geography of India > Explore > Between the Mountains and the Sea.

Government	
Religion	
Economic	
Art & Architecture	
Science & Technology	
Environment	
Social & Cultural Values	

Name _____ Date _____

EXPLORE: FOCUS QUESTIONS

Using what you learned from the Core Interactive Text, answer each page's focus question:

Between the Mountains and the Sea

What geographic features separate India from the rest of the continent of Asia?

_____
_____
_____

Rivers and River Valleys

What other geographic features affected life in India?

_____
_____
_____

Wet and Dry

How did ancient India's climate affect its civilizations?

_____
_____
_____

Civilization in the Indus Valley

How did civilizations arise on the Indian subcontinent?

_____
_____
_____

Mohenjo-daro

Why was Mohenjo-daro an important city in ancient India?

_____
_____
_____

Life in Ancient India's Major Cities

What innovations did the Indus Valley civilizations develop?

_____
_____

© Discovery Education | www.DiscoveryEducation.com

PROJECTS AND ASSESSMENTS

Explain Activities

ACTIVITY TYPE: ADVERTISEMENT

Geography of India

Imagine you are a city planner living during ancient times who wants to attract permanent settlers to Mohenjo-daro. In this activity, you will create an advertisement for Mohenjo-daro that highlights the city's geographic features.

ACTIVITY TYPE: DIAGRAM

Geography of India

Use at least 12 words from the word bank to create a graphic answer to the Essential Question. You may add any other words or symbols, but you must use all of the starred words. Summarize your map at the bottom and be prepared to present your thinking.

ACTIVITY TYPE: SOCIAL STUDIES EXPLANATION

Geography of India

In this Social Studies Explanation activity, you will use a template to assemble evidence from the sources you have explored. Then, you will write an answer to the Essential Question and defend your answer with supporting evidence.

Elaborate Activities

photo: Getty Images

INVESTIGATION TYPE: MAP-GUIDED INQUIRY

The Geography of India

How did geography influence the development of Indian civilization and culture? How does ancient India compare to modern India on a map? In this investigation, you will use the interactive Map-Guided Inquiry tool to analyze the impact of geography on Indian civilization and compare ancient India to modern India on a map.

ACTIVITY TYPE: PITCH YOUR IDEA

Indus Valley Math

In this activity, you will create a presentation to give before the Egyptian pharaoh explaining how the mathematical innovations of ancient India could improve his kingdom.

photo: NASA

PROJECTS AND ASSESSMENTS *(continued)*

photo: Bigstock

ACTIVITY TYPE: DOCUMENT-BASED INVESTIGATION

Monsoons: Blessing or Curse

Are the monsoons a blessing or curse for India?

Evaluate Activities

BRIEF-CONSTRUCTED RESPONSE (BCR)

Geography of India

EXTENDED-CONSTRUCTED RESPONSE (ECR)

Geography of India

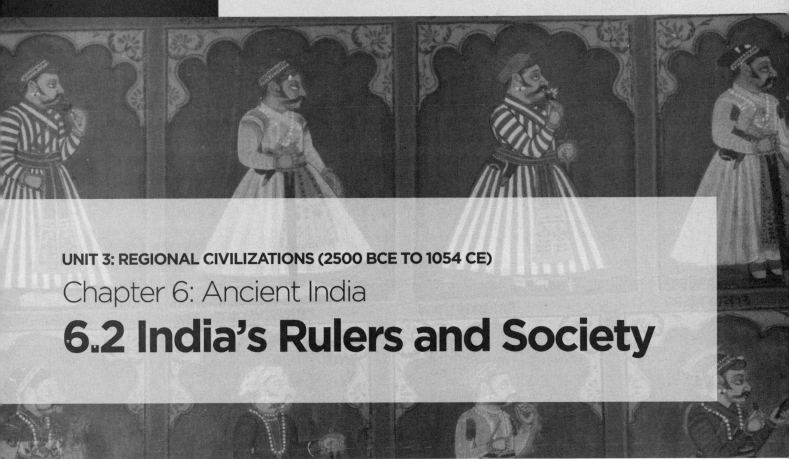

photo: The New York Public Library

UNIT 3: REGIONAL CIVILIZATIONS (2500 BCE TO 1054 CE)

Chapter 6: Ancient India

6.2 India's Rulers and Society

LESSON OVERVIEW

Lesson Objectives:

By the end of this lesson, you should be able to:

- Identify the cultural impact of the Aryan invasion.
- Describe the changes in territory and religion brought by the Mauryan and Gupta dynasties.
- Examine the Indian caste system from the perspective of members from various castes.

Lesson Essential Question:

What effects did India's social development and changing political powers have on the lives of people in ancient India?

Key Vocabulary

Ashoka, Bay of Bengal, Brahmans, Buddhism, caste system, Chandragupta, civilization, culture, Dalits/ Untouchables, dynasty, empire, Eurasia, Gupta Empire, Hinduism, Indo-European, Kshatriyas, Mauryan Emplre, merchant, nomadic, parliament, peasant, region, Siddhartha Gautama / Buddha, social class, society, Shudras, Taj Mahal, Vaisyas, Vedas

FLASHCARDS

1 ▶ The Vedic Period

Migrants called Aryans entered South Asia from the northwest around 1500 BCE and had a major cultural influence on the population already living there.

- **Religious traditions were written down in the Vedas and eventually developed into Hinduism**
- **The Aryans introduced the Sanskrit language. Sanskrit developed a written alphabet.**
- **During the Vedic Period, the early Vedas introduced varnas, religious distinctions between groups of people.**

Why Does It Matter?

The Aryans changed Indian culture and society forever. Hinduism remains the most prominent religion in India to this day, and the Sanskrit texts the Aryans helped write are the ancient scriptures used by the followers of this religion. Also, the caste system created a social order that still continues to impact social and political divisions in modern India.

photo: Pixabay
There are millions of gods and goddesses in Hinduism.

2 ▶ India's Caste System

The caste system in India developed over time. The religious varna system was combined with a system of jati castes – castes based on occupations.

- **The varna system consisted of five major groups: the Brahmans, the Kshatriyas, the Vaisyas, the Shudras, and the Dalits/Untouchables/Scheduled Caste.**
- **A person's jati caste often ruled his or her life. It determined things like occupation, who a person could marry, what a person could eat, and where a person lived.**
- **Discrimination based on the caste system was outlawed in 1949, but the caste system continues to create political and social divisions in India, particularly in rural areas**

Why Does It Matter?

The caste system has deeply influenced Indian culture and society for centuries. Dalits/Untouchables are still discriminated against in many places in the country.

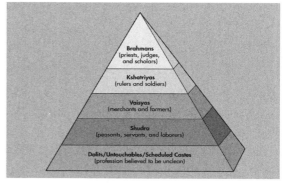

photo: Discovery Education
Deep-rooted beliefs about obligations and duties based on the caste system continue to affect people's lives in India.

Discovery EDUCATION | SOCIAL STUDIES TECHBOOK

FLASHCARDS *(continued)*

3 **Impact of the Mauryan and Gupta Empires**

Religious developments and other advances during the Mauryan and Gupta Empires had a strong impact on Indian society.

- Chandragupta Maurya created the Mauryan Empire.
- The Mauryan Empire connected most of India under one territory by conquering other states or local kingdoms.
- Emperor Ashoka was one of the most influential historical figures in ancient India.
- Ashoka converted to Buddhism and encouraged the spread of Buddhism in India.
- The rule of the Gupta Empire was seen as a golden age in India.
- Hinduism was revived during the Gupta reign.
- Artists and architects designed great statues and buildings devoted to Hinduism and Buddhism.
- Roads were built connecting the empire. Men attended universities and colleges.
- Gupta mathematicians developed a decimal system of writing and used zeroes as placeholders.

Why Does It Matter?

The Mauryan and Gupta Empires expanded the territory of India and contributed many advances and cultural beliefs to Indian society. Both Buddhism and Hinduism were kept alive and spread by these empires. Mathematical developments, such as using a zero as a placeholder, influenced our modern place value system.

photo: Corbis

Although ancient Egyptians and Arabs are often credited for modern math, evidence shows that much of our basic number system originated in India.

Name _____ **Date** _____

GRAPHIC ORGANIZER: Main Idea Web

Use this Main Idea Web to list characteristics about the Aryan people and their cultural beliefs. For supporting resources, go to Regional Civilizations > Ancient India > India's Rulers and Society > Explore > Vedic Period Cultural Contributions.

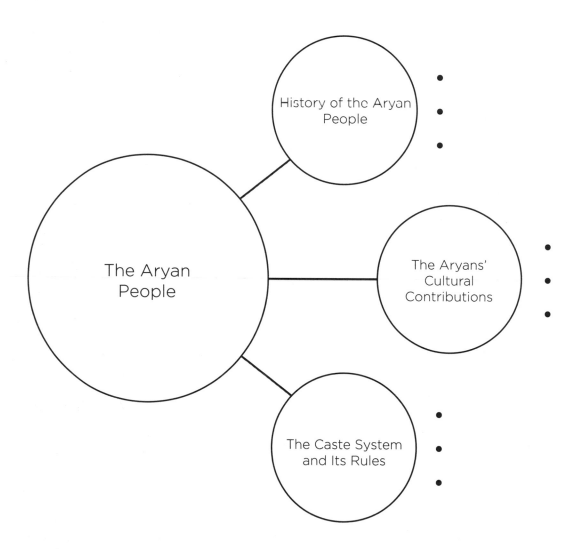

History of the Aryan People

-
-
-

The Aryan People

The Aryans' Cultural Contributions

-
-
-

The Caste System and Its Rules

-
-
-

Name _____ Date _____

EXPLORE: FOCUS QUESTIONS

Using what you learned from the Core Interactive Text, answer each page's focus question:

The Vedic Period Begins
Who were the Aryans?

_____

_____

_____

Vedic Period Cultural Contributions
How did the Vedic period influence the culture of India?

_____

_____

_____

The Caste System
What is the caste system?

_____

_____

_____

Rules of the Caste System
How did the caste system work?

_____

_____

_____

The Mauryan Empire
Who was Chandragupta Maurya?

_____

_____

_____

Name _____ **Date** _____

EXPLORE: FOCUS QUESTIONS *(continued)*

Ashoka and Buddhism
What did Emperor Ashoka accomplish?

_____
_____
_____
_____

The Gupta Empire
What was the Gupta Empire and how did it impact Indian culture?

_____
_____
_____

Achievements of the Gupta Empire
What advances were made during the Gupta Empire?

_____
_____
_____

PROJECTS AND ASSESSMENTS

Explain Activities

ACTIVITY TYPE: VISUALIZATION

Cartoons of Ancient India

Use this Storyboard template to create a comic strip showing how a particular person, group of people, or event had an impact on Indian society over time.

ACTIVITY TYPE: DIAGRAM

Venn Diagram

In this activity, you will use a Venn diagram to compare and contrast the caste system of ancient India with the social pyramids of ancient Egypt or Mesopotamia.

ACTIVITY TYPE: SOCIAL STUDIES EXPLANATION

India's Rulers and Society

In this Social Studies Explanation activity, you will use a template to assemble evidence from the sources you have explored. Then, you will write an answer to the Essential Question and defend your answer with supporting evidence.

Elaborate Activities

photo: Associated Press

INVESTIGATION TYPE: TIMELINE INQUIRY

India's Caste System

Does the caste system affect everyday life in India today? How is the caste system evident in modern Indian society?

ACTIVITY TYPE: YOU AS ARTIST

Ashoka's Memorial

Imagine that the government of India is planning to dedicate a monument to Ashoka's rule. In this activity, you will first decide what Ashoka should be remembered most for. Then, you will submit a design for the monument in the form of a simple drawing. You will also include a letter describing how your design for the monument shows elements of Ashoka's personality in one role or the other. You will explain why Ashoka should be remembered more for his military achievements or for his achievements as a Buddhist emperor, using historical evidence to support your position.

PROJECTS AND ASSESSMENTS *(continued)*

photo: Los Angeles County Museum of Art (www.lacma.org)

ACTIVITY TYPE: ROLE PLAY

Life in My Caste

Imagine that you are living in ancient India in the year 200 BCE. What is life like for you? In this activity, you will research the major castes in ancient Indian society and write a diary entry that depicts daily life for you as a member of one of the castes. You will use historical evidence to write your diary entry.

photo: Library of Congress

ACTIVITY TYPE: DOCUMENT-BASED INVESTIGATION

Aryan Impact on India

In this activity, you will write a speech explaining the impact the ancient Aryans have had on the culture and society of India over time.

Evaluate Activities

BRIEF-CONSTRUCTED RESPONSE (BCR)

India's Rulers and Society

EXTENDED-CONSTRUCTED RESPONSE (ECR)

India's Rulers and Society

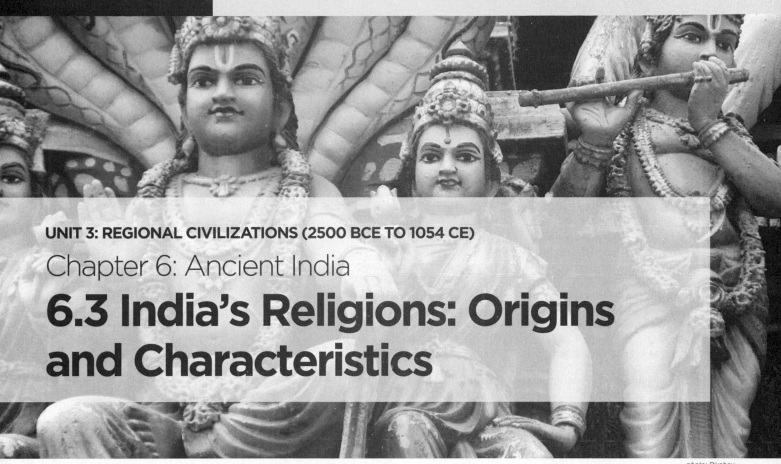

photo: Pixabay

UNIT 3: REGIONAL CIVILIZATIONS (2500 BCE TO 1054 CE)

Chapter 6: Ancient India

6.3 India's Religions: Origins and Characteristics

LESSON OVERVIEW

Lesson Objectives:

By the end of this lesson, you should be able to:

- Connect the beliefs of Hinduism to the caste system and other elements of ancient Indian life.
- Compare Buddhism to other ancient religions (including Hinduism and Egyptian/ Mesopotamian religions).
- Analyze the motives for and impact of Ashoka's conversion to Buddhism.

Lesson Essential Question:

How did religion influence Indian society?

Key Vocabulary

Angkor, Aryans, Ashoka, avatars, beginning of Buddhism, beginning of Hinduism, Bhagavad Gita, Brahma, Buddhism, Chandragupta, culture, Dalits/ Untouchables, dharma, Eightfold Path, Four Noble Truths, Hinduism, Jainism, karma, Krishna, Mahabharata, Mauryan Empire, nirvana, Rama, reincarnation, Sanskrit, Shiva, Siddhartha Gautama/ Buddha, Vaisyas, Vedas, Vishnu

FLASHCARDS

1 Hinduism

Hinduism arose among the Aryan invaders of India around 1500 BCE. Though modern India is a land of many religions, Hindu beliefs and practices are the most dominant.

- Hinduism has no specific founder.
- Hindus believe in many gods and goddesses, all of whom are aspects of a single universal god, Brahma. All human souls are a part of Brahma.
- Hindus are expected to carry out their duties, or dharma. They believe in reincarnation, the idea that the soul is reborn in an endless cycle of life and death.
- How well a person carries out his or her dharma determines his or her karma, which in turn determines that person's status in his or her next life. The dharma of an individual is closely tied to his or her caste, gender, and age.
- The Mahabharata is the great Indian epic. It was completed about 400 CE under the Gupta Empire. The most important part is the Bhagavad Gita, which Hindus consider one of their most sacred scriptures.

Why Does It Matter?

Hindus believe that the caste system is inseparable from their religion. The dharma of the different castes is an idea set forth by the god Krishna in the Bhagavad-Gita. An individual's adherence to dharma impacts his or her karma, which Hindus believe determines that individual's status in his or her next lives. The caste system continues to influence Indian society even today.

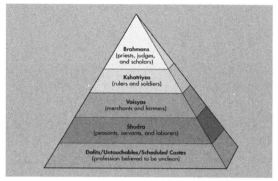

photo: Discovery Education

India's modern leaders have tried to do away with the caste system, but it still remains an important cultural influence in some regions.

2 Buddhism

Buddhism arose out of Hinduism and shares some of its beliefs and practices. It is a religion in which the idea of God is not important.

- Buddhism was founded by Prince Siddhartha Gautama, who became the Buddha through enlightenment.
- Buddhism is based on the teachings of the Buddha as he set them forth in the Four Noble Truths and the Eightfold Path. These ideas are based on the Hindu concept of dharma.
- The Buddha accepted the Hindu ideas of karma and reincarnation but taught that people can free themselves from rebirth through meditation and by following the Eightfold Path.
- After the Buddha's death, his followers continued to spread his teachings throughout India.

Why Does It Matter?

Buddhism is different from Hinduism and other ancient religions in that it is not founded on gods or rituals that must be carried out by priests. Its goal is enlightenment, which individuals are capable of achieving for themselves. Though it adopted some Hindu beliefs, it is not tied to Indian culture, and it has spread to peoples of many cultures.

photo: Pixabay

This colossal statue of the Buddha sits outside a Buddhist temple.

FLASHCARDS *(continued)*

3 ▶ Ashoka's Conversion

Ashoka, the third Mauryan emperor, became a Buddhist and played a large role in spreading Buddhism throughout Asia.

- Ashoka was a warrior and conqueror who renounced his warlike ways and became a Buddhist.
- He had laws based on Buddhist teachings inscribed on pillars throughout India and had mounds called stupas constructed to hold Buddhist sacred objects.
- He sent missionaries to other parts of Asia to spread the teachings of the Buddha.

Why Does It Matter?

Though few Indians are Buddhists today, the teachings of the Buddha have become part of India's culture. Ashoka's conversion and missionary efforts throughout the region spread Buddhism to other areas such as Japan and China, where it remains popular today.

The pillars Ashoka inscribed with Buddhist precepts are found everywhere in India—even on postage stamps.

Name _____ Date _____

GRAPHIC ORGANIZER: Vocabulary Chart

Use this Vocabulary Chart to explore the definition of *Hinduism*. For supporting resources, go to Regional Civilizations > Ancient India > India's Religions: Origins and Characteristics > Explore > Hinduism.

DEFINITION:

Personal:

Dictionary:

EXAMPLES (Drawn or Written):

TERM:
Hinduism

SENTENCES:

Teacher/Book:

Personal:

RELATED:

WORD PARTS:

Outside of School (Who Would Use the Word? How Would He or She Use It?):

Name _____ Date _____

GRAPHIC ORGANIZER: Comparison Chart

Use this Comparison Chart to take notes on Hindu gods and goddesses. For supporting resources, go to Regional Civilizations > Ancient India > India's Religions: Origins and Characteristics > Explore > Hindu Gods and Goddesses.

Criteria	What Physical Form Does the God/Goddess Take?	What Meaning Does the Deity Have to Hindus?	What Characteristics Does the God/Goddess Have?
Brahma			
Vishnu			
Krishna			
Rama			
Shiva			
Shakti			

Name _____ **Date** _____

GRAPHIC ORGANIZER: Comparison Chart

Use this Comparison Chart to compare and contrast Hindu and Buddhist history, practices, and beliefs. For supporting resources, go to Regional Civilizations > Ancient India > India's Religions: Origins and Characteristics > Explore > Dharma and Karma.

Criteria	Hinduism	Buddhism
Goal of Religion		
Founder		
Origins		
Beliefs		
Practices		

© Discovery Education | www.DiscoveryEducation.com

Name _____ **Date** _____

GRAPHIC ORGANIZER: Cause/Event/Effect Chart

Use this Cause/Event/Effect Chart to trace Ashoka's conversion to Buddhism. For supporting resources, go to Regional Civilizations > Ancient India > India's Religions: Origins and Characteristics > Explore > The Warrior Who Embraced Peace.

Cause	Event	Effect

Name _____ **Date** _____

EXPLORE: FOCUS QUESTIONS

Using what you learned from the Core Interactive Text, answer each page's focus question:

Hinduism

What do Hindus believe?

_____
_____
_____

Hindu Gods and Goddesses

What gods and goddesses hold special importance in Hinduism?

_____
_____
_____

Dharma and Karma

What does Hinduism teach people about how to live?

_____
_____
_____

India's Epic Story

How is the Indian social structure reflected in Hindu writings?

_____
_____
_____

Prince Gautama Becomes the Buddha

How did Buddhism begin?

_____
_____
_____

Name _____   Date _____

EXPLORE: FOCUS QUESTIONS *(continued)*

The Four Noble Truths and the Eightfold Path
What were the teachings of Buddha?

_____

_____

_____

The Warrior Who Embraced Peace
Why did Ashoka convert to Buddhism?

_____

_____

_____

A Religious Revolution
How did Ashoka's conversion to Buddhism change India?

_____

_____

_____

PROJECTS AND ASSESSMENTS

Explain Activities

ACTIVITY TYPE: DIAGRAM

Brahma, Amun, and Nirvana

Use at least 12 words from the word bank to create a graphic answer to the question: How do Hinduism, Buddhism, and ancient Egyptian religion compare? You may add any other words or symbols, but you must use all of the starred words. Summarize your map at the bottom and be prepared to present your thinking. Specific areas of comparison might include founders, gods, structure, leaders, rules, and societal influence.

ACTIVITY TYPE: QUICK WRITE

One God or Many?

Think about what you learned from reading the text and watching the videos. Use information gathered from these texts and media to complete a paragraph.

ACTIVITY TYPE: SOCIAL STUDIES EXPLANATION

India's Religions: Origins and Characteristics

In this Social Studies Explanation activity, you will use a template to assemble evidence from the sources you have explored. Then, you will write an answer to the Essential Question and defend your answer with supporting evidence.

Elaborate Activities

photo: Getty Images

INVESTIGATION TYPE: SOURCE ANALYSIS

Hindu Religious Art

How does Hindu worship depend on artistic expression? In this investigation, you will analyze statues of three important Hindu gods—Brahma, Vishnu, and Shiva—to explore the connection between Hindu art and spiritual beliefs.

PROJECTS AND ASSESSMENTS *(continued)*

photo: Getty Images

INVESTIGATION TYPE: TIMELINE MAP

Trade and Religion

How did trade affect the expansion of major religions across Southeast Asia? In this investigation, you will use the Timeline Map interactive tool to examine historical trade routes and determine how they are connected with the expansion of major religions across various countries of this region.

ACTIVITY TYPE: EXPRESS YOUR OPINION

Ashoka Changes His Ways

In this activity, imagine that you are a reporter in ancient India, assigned to write a commentary on Ashoka's conversion to Buddhism and its impact on the empire. You will study stories and create a news report with interviews of Ashoka and others. Then, you will write an editorial using the commentaries and quotes to express your opinion on the new policies and what they may mean for India.

photo: Getty Images

ACTIVITY TYPE: SAY WHAT?

The Bhagavad Gita

Professor Know-It-All would like to publish an illustrated modern translation of the Bhagavad Gita for students, and he needs your help. In this activity, you will read a portion of Chapter 4 of the Bhagavad Gita, translate it, and diagram it for modern readers.

Evaluate Activities

BRIEF-CONSTRUCTED RESPONSE (BCR)

India's Religions

EXTENDED-CONSTRUCTED RESPONSE (ECR)

India's Religions

photo: Getty Images

UNIT 3: REGIONAL CIVILIZATIONS (2500 BCE TO 1054 CE)

Chapter 7: Ancient China

7.1 Geography of China

LESSON OVERVIEW

Lesson Objectives:

By the end of this lesson, you should be able to:

- Locate ancient China and its important cities and rivers on a historical map and a modern map.
- Analyze the connection between ancient China's location and its growth and expansion.

Lesson Essential Question:

How did China's location impact its development?

Key Vocabulary

Anyang, Asia, Beijing, Chang'an, China, Cishan, dynasty, Gobi Desert, Great Wall of China, Han dynasty, Himalayas, Huang He River, latitude, longitude, Luoyang, Mekong River, Mount Everest, North China Plain, Qin dynasty, Qinling Mountains, Shang dynasty, Silk Road, Tibetan Plateau, Xianyang

© Discovery Education | www.DiscoveryEducation.com

FLASHCARDS

1 The Location of China

The borders of China have changed over time, but the center of Chinese society has always been located in the eastern and central plains. This is the area between the two great rivers in China, and it supported the development of ancient China's largest cities.

- The Chang Jiang and the Huang He rivers are located in the eastern and central plains.
- The Chang Jiang and the Huang He provided fresh water and rich soil necessary for the establishment of the earliest civilizations.
- Cishan and Banpo were two of the earliest known civilizations in China.
- Major cities in ancient China included Xianyang, Chang'an, and Luoyang.

Why Does It Matter?

Like most civilizations, Chinese civilization developed close to major sources of water. Rivers provided drinking water and also added silt to the soil in the river valleys, making agriculture possible. China's earliest major cities developed near the water.

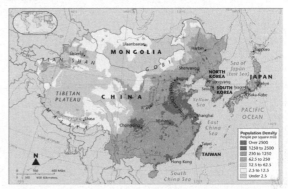

photo: Discovery Education

Notice that the darkest colors on this map of China are in the areas near the major rivers. This is also where early ancient cities were developed. The proximity to water remains important to modern civilization.

2 Deserts, Mountains, and Nomads Impact Chinese Expansion and Trade

Most Chinese dynasties sought to expand their empires' borders. Geography limited where the Chinese could expand. The location and size of the Gobi Desert and the Himalayan Mountains restricted the borders of China. Nomads in the north were often able to fight back against the Chinese, further preventing their expansion. These same factors made travel for merchants and traders difficult.

- Chinese expansion was blocked to the west by the Gobi Desert and to the southwest by the Himalayas.
- Chinese expansion to the north was blocked by the nomadic horsemen who lived in Mongolia.
- Trade between China and its neighbors relied on difficult overland routes or sea voyages.

Why Does It Matter?

The geographic features of China played a major role in the development of its civilization. These same features continue to impact life in China today.

photo: Discovery Education

The geography of China played a major role in its development.

Name _____ **Date** _____

GRAPHIC ORGANIZER: Change Over Time Chart

Use this Change Over Time Chart to explain how boundaries and rivers impacted the development of China. For supporting resources, go to Regional Civilizations > Ancient China > Geography of China > Explore > Ancient China.

Before:	After:

Changes:

Name _____ **Date** _____

GRAPHIC ORGANIZER: Summary Frames

Use these Summary Frames to illustrate scenes from early Chinese civilizations. For supporting resources, go to Regional Civilizations > Ancient China > Geography of China > Explore > China's Earliest Civilizations.

Name _____ **Date** _____

 GRAPHIC ORGANIZER: Sequencing Chart

Use this Sequencing Chart to record notes about the important cities for each dynasty. For supporting resources, go to Regional Civilizations > Ancient China > Geography of China > Explore > China's Ancient Cities.

City	Date	Summary

Name _____ **Date** _____

GRAPHIC ORGANIZER: Sequencing Chart *(continued)*

City	Date	Summary

Name _____ Date _____

GRAPHIC ORGANIZER: Costs/Benefits Chart

Use this Costs/Benefits Chart to compare the effects of deserts and mountains on Chinese expansion. For supporting resources, go to Regional Civilizations > Ancient China > Geography of China > Explore > China's Great Deserts.

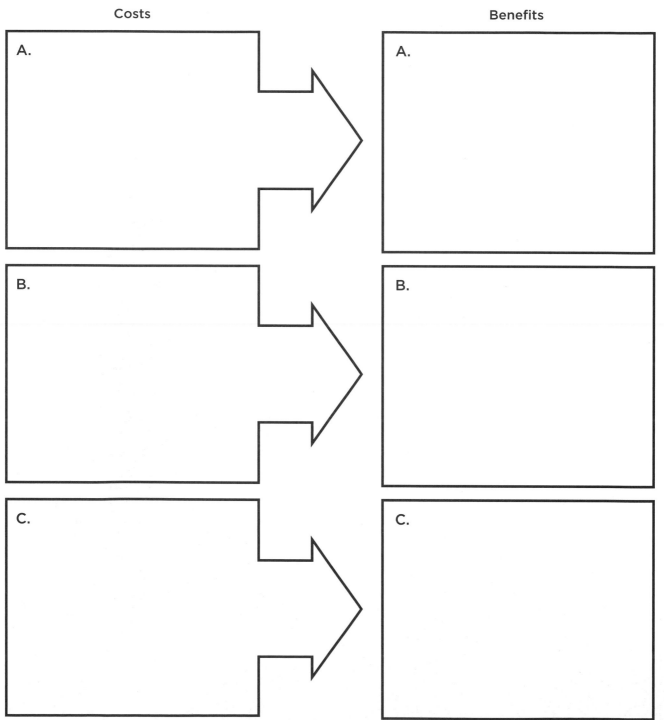

Costs

A.

B.

C.

Benefits

A.

B.

C.

Name _____ **Date** _____

GRAPHIC ORGANIZER: Summary Frames

Use these Summary Frames to illustrate scenes showing possible interactions between the northern nomads and the Chinese. For supporting resources, go to Regional Civilizations > Ancient China > Geography of China > Explore > Nomadic Horsemen to the North.

_____ _____ _____

_____ _____ _____

_____ _____ _____

_____ _____ _____

_____ _____ _____

_____ _____ _____

Name _____ **Date** _____

GRAPHIC ORGANIZER: Cause/Event/Effect Chart

Use this Cause/Event/Effect Chart to explain the role of China's geography in its relations with other civilizations. For supporting resources, go to Regional Civilizations > Ancient China > Geography of China > Explore > The Trading Networks of Ancient China.

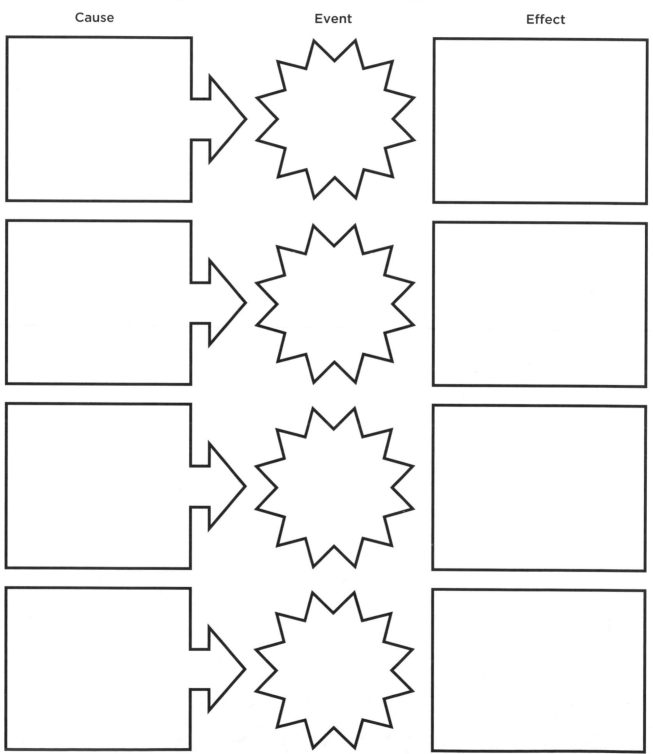

Cause   **Event**   **Effect**

© Discovery Education | www.DiscoveryEducation.com

Name _____   Date _____

EXPLORE: FOCUS QUESTIONS

Using what you learned from the Core Interactive Text, answer each page's focus question:

Ancient China
Where is China located?

_____

_____

_____

China's Earliest Civilizations
What were ancient China's earliest civilizations?

_____

_____

_____

China's Ancient Cities
Where were ancient China's most important cities located?

_____

_____

_____

China's Great Deserts
How did nearby deserts both benefit and restrict the Chinese?

_____

_____

_____

The Himalayas
How did the mountains both benefit and restrict the Chinese?

_____

_____

_____

Name _____ Date _____

EXPLORE: FOCUS QUESTIONS *(continued)*

Nomadic Horsemen to the North
How did the Chinese interact with the nomadic groups to the north?

_____
_____
_____

The Trading Networks of Ancient China
How did China's geography impact its interactions with other civilizations?

_____
_____
_____

PROJECTS AND ASSESSMENTS

Explain Activities

ACTIVITY TYPE: DIAGRAM

Comparing Ancient River Civilizations

In this activity, you will compare and contrast the economic, political, social, and religious institutions of four ancient river civilizations. Then, you will summarize the similarities and differences among these civilizations.

ACTIVITY TYPE: MOVIE TRAILER

The Nomads

Use story frames to sketch out a trailer for a movie about the nomadic groups to the north of ancient China. The trailer should help the producers understand the relationship between the Chinese and the nomads.

ACTIVITY TYPE: ENCYCLOPEDIA ENTRY

Geographic Features of Ancient China

In this activity, you will create an encyclopedia entry for one of China's major geographic features.

ACTIVITY TYPE: SOCIAL STUDIES EXPLANATION

Geography of China

In this Social Studies Explanation activity, you will use a template to assemble evidence from the sources you have explored. Then, you will write an answer to the Essential Question and defend your answer with supporting evidence.

Elaborate Activities

photo: Getty Images

INVESTIGATION TYPE: MAP-GUIDED INQUIRY

Geography of China

How did geography influence the development of civilization in ancient China? In this investigation, you will use the Map-Guided Inquiry interactive tool to examine how ancient China compares to modern China on a map.

PROJECTS AND ASSESSMENTS *(continued)*

photo: IRC

ACTIVITY TYPE: ROLE PLAY

Ancient China's Silk Road

Imagine that you are a trader who is making the journey along ancient China's Silk Road. You begin your journey in Samarkand and travel to Lanzhou. Write a journal entry that highlights the locations, sights, and people you encounter and the experiences you have during your journey.

photo: Getty Images

ACTIVITY TYPE: CURRENT EVENTS CONNECTION

The Three Gorges Dam

In this activity, you will conduct research about the costs and benefits of the Three Gorges Dam and prepare a presentation either supporting or opposing construction of the dam.

photo: Getty Images

ACTIVITY TYPE: DOCUMENT-BASED INVESTIGATION

Geography of China: Beneficial or Harmful?

In this activity, you will write either a letter to city leaders or an editorial to a newspaper, explaining why the rivers, mountains, and deserts have impeded or advanced the development of Chinese civilization.

Evaluate Activities

BRIEF-CONSTRUCTED RESPONSE (BCR)

Geography of China

EXTENDED-CONSTRUCTED RESPONSE (ECR)

Geography of China

photo: Getty Images

UNIT 3: REGIONAL CIVILIZATIONS (2500 BCE TO 1054 CE)

Chapter 7: Ancient China

7.2 China's Belief Systems

LESSON OVERVIEW

Lesson Objectives:

By the end of this lesson, you should be able to:

- Identify Confucius, his teachings, and his contributions to the growth of Confucianism in China.

- Compare Confucianism with other major philosophies of ancient China based on their views of human nature and their implications for government.

Key Vocabulary

beginning of Confucianism, China, Confucianism, Confucius, dynasty, filial piety, Han dynasty, Han Feizi, Laozi, Legalism, philosophy, Qin dynasty, Taoism, Warring States period

Lesson Essential Question:

How did Confucianism, Daoism, and Legalism influence society in ancient China?

FLASHCARDS

1 Confucianism

Confucianism is a philosophy that began more than 2,000 years ago in China.

- In response to the chaos of the Warring States period, Confucius became interested in creating a harmonious and just society.
- He believed rulers must act correctly and set a good example for their subjects.
- He defined four hierarchical relationships—father and son, ruler and subject, husband and wife, and older brother and younger brother—and one egalitarian relationship: friend and friend.
- He described how people should act in each of these relationships to ensure a peaceful society.

Why Does It Matter?

The ideas of Confucianism influenced the leadership of the Han dynasty. It awarded positions to government officials based on merit rather than on status or connections. Confucianism continues to affect Chinese society today. Chinese culture can be better understood by examining the ideas of Confucius.

photo: Pixabay

This is a representation of Confucius. What can you learn about him from this image?

2 Daoism and Legalism

Daoism and Legalism are two different philosophies that began toward the end of the Zhou dynasty. They offer very different perspectives on how to attain a peaceful and ordered society.

- Laozi is believed to be the founder of Daoism.
- Daoists believe that all power comes from the Dao, and that humans should strive to live simple lives in balance with nature.
- Daoism has affected Chinese culture in areas such as medicine, calligraphy, and literature.
- Han Feizi was the founder of Legalism.
- Han Feizi believed humans were selfish and that rulers needed to establish strict rules and harsh punishments to rule effectively.

Why Does It Matter?

Daoism and Legalism offered different solutions and approaches to creating an ordered society. The Qin dynasty used the principles of Legalism to establish one of the first empires of China. Daoism was occasionally used as the basis of civil service exams and affected many aspects of Chinese culture.

photo: Los Angeles County Museum of Art (www.lacma.org)

Daoism, like Confucianism and Legalism, sought to find a way to create an ordered and peaceful society.

Name _____ Date _____

GRAPHIC ORGANIZER: Comparison Chart

Use this Comparison Chart to compare the three major philosophies of China. For supporting resources, go to Regional Civilizations > Ancient China > China's Belief Systems > Explore > A State of War.

	Criteria	Confucianism	Daoism	Legalism
What Was Life Like in the Zhou Dynasty?	How to Achieve Harmony and Order			
	Instructions to Rulers			
How Did the Zhou Dynasty Influence Philosophers?	Instructions for Daily Life			
	Influences on Chinese Culture and Government			

Name _____ Date _____

EXPLORE: FOCUS QUESTIONS

Using what you learned from the Core Interactive Text, answer each page's focus question:

A State of War

Why did the three major philosophies of China all develop during the same era?

_____
_____
_____
_____

Confucius

Who was Confucius?

_____
_____
_____

The Beliefs of Confucianism

What were the main ideas of Confucianism?

_____
_____
_____
_____

The Influence of Confucianism

How did Confucianism influence Chinese government?

_____
_____
_____

Daoism and Nature

What other important philosophies were developed during this time?

_____
_____
_____

Name _____ Date _____

EXPLORE: FOCUS QUESTIONS *(continued)*

Daoism's Impact on Chinese Society
How did Daoism affect Chinese Society?

_____

_____

_____

Legalism and its Influence
How did Legalism influence Chinese society?

_____

_____

_____

PROJECTS AND ASSESSMENTS

Explain Activities

ACTIVITY TYPE: DIAGRAM

China's Belief Systems

Use at least 10 words from the word bank to create a graphic answer to the Essential Question for one of the philosophies discussed in the text. You may add any other words or symbols, but you must use all of the starred words. Summarize your map at the bottom and be prepared to present your thinking.

ACTIVITY TYPE: QUICK WRITE

Confucianism in Government Today

In this Quick Write, you will use information gathered from text, media, and graphic organizers you completed to write a paragraph answering the following questions: Which parts of Confucianism do you think could be applied to American society and government today? Which could not?

ACTIVITY TYPE: SOCIAL STUDIES EXPLANATION

China's Belief Systems

In this Social Studies Explanation activity, you will use a template to assemble evidence from the sources you have explored. Then, you will write an answer to the Essential Question and defend your answer with supporting evidence.

Elaborate Activities

INVESTIGATION TYPE: ENDURING DEBATE

Confucius vs. Han Feizi

In this activity, you will explore a debate on the following question: What are the roles of individuals and government in society? Then, you will vote for the position with which you agree more.

PROJECTS AND ASSESSMENTS *(continued)*

photo: Getty Images

ACTIVITY TYPE: CURRENT EVENTS CONNECTION

Ancient Beliefs in Modern China

Imagine you are a consultant with the U.S. State Department. Your supervisor has asked you to teach a lesson on the effects of China's ancient belief systems on life in China today. Create an interactive slideshow to accompany your lecture that captures the key points of your lesson.

photo: Pixabay

ACTIVITY TYPE: SOCRATIC SEMINAR

Philosophy and Government

In this Socratic Seminar, you will read excerpts from texts by Confucius and Laozi and complete a discussion that leads to a response to the question: Which system would be best for running a country and why?

Evaluate Activities

BRIEF-CONSTRUCTED RESPONSE (BCR)

China's Belief Systems

EXTENDED-CONSTRUCTED RESPONSE (ECR)

China's Belief Systems

UNIT 3: REGIONAL CIVILIZATIONS (2500 BCE TO 1054 CE)

Chapter 7: Ancient China

7.3 Life in the Chinese Dynasties

LESSON OVERVIEW

Lesson Objectives:

By the end of this lesson, you should be able to:

- Trace the important Chinese dynasties (Zhou dynasty, Qin dynasty, Han dynasty) and analyze impacts of these dynasties on life in East Asia.
- Analyze the societal structures in China during this period.

Lesson Essential Question:

How did the Chinese dynasties affect life throughout East Asia?

Key Vocabulary

China, Confucianism, Confucius, dynasty, emperor, Emperor Wu Di, feudalism, Forbidden City, Great Wall of China, Han dynasty, Huns, Laozi, Li Yuan, Liu Bang, mandate, Mandate of Heaven, Marco Polo, meritocracy, Ming dynasty, Qin, Qin dynasty, Qin Shi Huang Di, Roman Empire, Silk Road, Song dynasty, Warring States period, Xuan Zang, Zheng He, Zhou dynasty

FLASHCARDS

1 The Impact of the Zhou, Qin, and Han Dynasties

The Zhou, Qin, and Han dynasties had a strong influence on life in East Asia.

- The Zhou introduced the idea of the Mandate of Heaven, which was also used by the Qin and Han dynasties.
- The Zhou established a feudal system in China.
- The Qin united China, creating the first Chinese empire.
- Qin Shi Huang Di constructed the Great Wall of China and created a strong central government that was copied by following dynasties.
- The Han dynasty expanded China's territory and helped to establish trade routes that spread Chinese goods and culture to the West.
- The Han established a system of merit based on the teachings of Confucius that was used to place government officials.
- The Han supported the arts and science, which led to the creation of great artistic and literary works and technological inventions.

Why Does It Matter?

The achievements of the Chinese dynasties, such as setting up an organized central government, adopting Confucianism, and inventing paper, had a strong influence on life throughout East Asia.

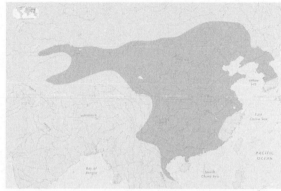

photo: Discovery Education

Each of the early Chinese dynasties played an important role in China's history.

2 The Structure of Society in Ancient China

The ancient Chinese developed a structure for government and family that was based on the teachings of Confucius.

- The Han established a government bureaucracy and chose officials based on merit.
- The ancient Chinese family system considered males superior to females and gave fathers complete legal authority over their wives and children.
- Many generations of the same family often lived together. The elder members of the family were treated with great respect and had authority over younger family members.

Why Does It Matter?

The style of government established by the Han dynasty was the basis for a number of similar systems throughout history. The family system in China changed dramatically during the 1900s, but it is still influenced somewhat by the teachings of Confucius.

The above image shows an ancient statue of Confucius. Behind this statute are two statues of his followers.

Name _____ **Date** _____

GRAPHIC ORGANIZER: Main Idea Web

Use this Main Idea Web to record important ideas about feudalism. For supporting resources, go to Regional Civilizations > Ancient China > Life in the Chinese Dynasties > Explore > Feudalism in China.

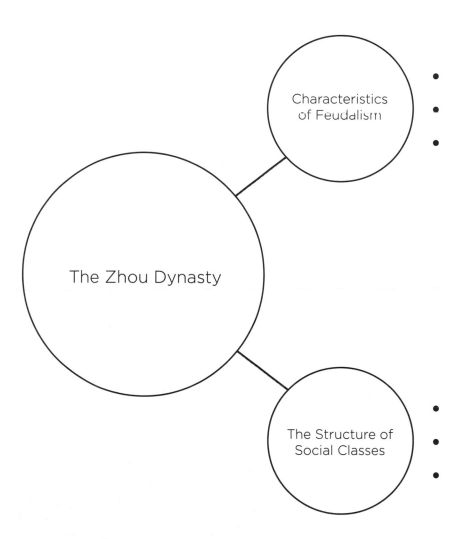

SOCIAL STUDIES
TECHBOOK

Name _____ **Date** _____

GRAPHIC ORGANIZER: Cause/Event/Effect Chart

Use this Cause/Event/Effect Chart to analyze the causes and effects of the Zhou dynasty's decline and the Warring States period. For supporting resources, go to Regional Civilizations > Ancient China > Life in the Chinese Dynasties > Explore > The Warring States.

Cause	Event	Effect

Name _____ **Date** _____

 GRAPHIC ORGANIZER: Main Idea Web

Use this Main Idea Web to record important characteristics and achievements of the Qin dynasty. For supporting resources, go to Regional Civilizations > Ancient China > Life in the Chinese Dynasties > Explore > The First Chinese Empire.

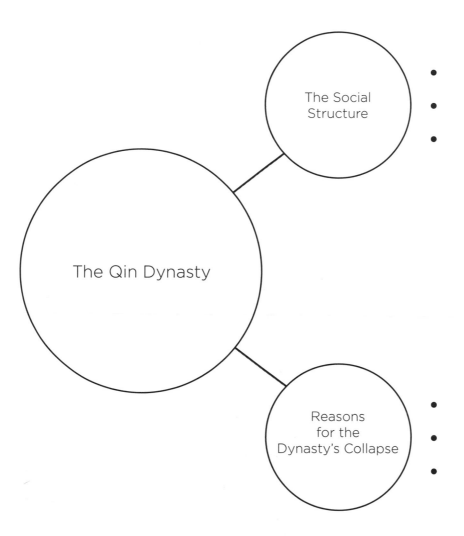

The Social Structure

-
-
-

The Qin Dynasty

Reasons for the Dynasty's Collapse

-
-
-

Name _____ Date _____

GRAPHIC ORGANIZER: GREASES Chart

Use this GREASES Chart to examine elements of Han government, culture, and society. For supporting resources, go to Regional Civilizations > Ancient China > Life in the Chinese Dynasties > Explore > The Han Dynasty.

Government	
Religion	
Economic	
Art & **A**rchitecture	
Science & **T**echnology	
Environment	
Social & **C**ultural Values	

Name _____   Date _____

EXPLORE: FOCUS QUESTIONS

Using what you learned from the Core Interactive Text, answer each page's focus question:

The Zhou Dynasty Forms

How did the Zhou dynasty influence China?

_____
_____
_____
_____

Feudalism in China

How did the Zhou rulers maintain control over their empire?

_____
_____
_____
_____

The Warring States

Why did the Zhou dynasty decline?

_____
_____
_____
_____

The First Chinese Empire

How did the Qin dynasty unify China?

_____
_____
_____
_____

The Impact and Collapse of the Qin Dynasty

What were the major achievements of the Qin dynasty?

_____
_____
_____

Name _____ Date _____

EXPLORE: FOCUS QUESTIONS *(continued)*

The Han Dynasty
How did the Han dynasty expand China?

_____

_____

_____

Life During the Han Dynasty
How was society structured during the Han dynasty?

_____

_____

_____

Government During the Han Dynasty
How was government structured during the Han dynasty?

_____

_____

_____

The Decline and Legacy of the Han Dynasty
What were the major achievements of the Han dynasty and why did it collapse?

_____

_____

_____

PROJECTS AND ASSESSMENTS

Explain Activities

ACTIVITY TYPE: VISUALIZATION

Life in the Chinese Dynasties

Use the frames to draw pictures that show what life was like in each of the following dynastic periods: Zhou, Qin, and Han. Below each frame, write a caption that describes what is happening or what is being shown in each picture.

ACTIVITY TYPE: DIAGRAM

Life in the Chinese Dynasties

In this activity, you will complete a Comparison Chart and write a two-paragraph summary of your comparison. Describe both the similarities and the differences among the three dynasties.

ACTIVITY TYPE: SOCIAL STUDIES EXPLANATION

Life in the Chinese Dynasties

In this Social Studies Explanation activity, you will use a template to assemble evidence from the sources you have explored. Then, you will write an answer to the Essential Question and defend your answer with supporting evidence.

Elaborate Activities

photo: Discovery Education

INVESTIGATION TYPE: HISTORICAL PERSPECTIVES

Life in China During the Qin Dynasty

Your mission is to meet four individuals from the Qin dynasty. After reading their profiles, decide what perspective each person might have had on key issues of the day.

PROJECTS AND ASSESSMENTS *(continued)*

photo: Pixabay

ACTIVITY TYPE: ROLE PLAY

Job Interview in the Han Dynasty

First, you will need to analyze Confucian teachings to understand how his ideas influenced society. Then, you will prepare for the role of the interviewer by drafting a list of interview questions based on how you think Confucian beliefs and ideas can be used to help you select the best job candidate. Finally, you will conduct the interview with your partner, who is playing the role of the job candidate, and take notes on his or her responses.

photo: Library of Congress

ACTIVITY TYPE: CLASSROOM DEBATE

The Impact of Qin Shi Huang Di

As you will learn in this activity, Qin Shi Huang Di was one of the most powerful emperors who ever ruled China. However, did he have more of a positive or a negative impact on this country? At your meeting with your fellow scholars, you will debate the following topic: "Resolved: Qin Shi Huang Di had a positive impact on China."

Evaluate Activities

BRIEF-CONSTRUCTED RESPONSE (BCR)

Life in the Chinese Dynasties

EXTENDED-CONSTRUCTED RESPONSE (ECR)

Life in the Chinese Dynasties

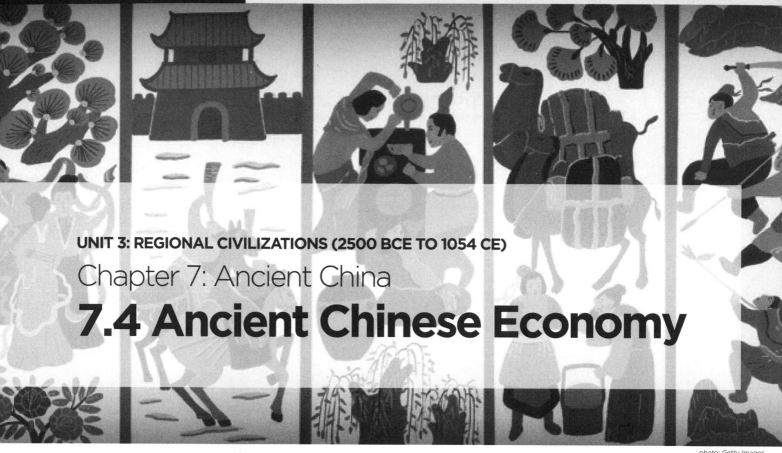

photo: Getty Images

UNIT 3: REGIONAL CIVILIZATIONS (2500 BCE TO 1054 CE)

Chapter 7: Ancient China

7.4 Ancient Chinese Economy

LESSON OVERVIEW

Lesson Objectives:

By the end of this lesson, you should be able to:

- Trace the land and sea routes of the Silk Road.
- Analyze the importance of the Silk Road to trade and economic growth in ancient China and for cultural diffusion throughout the world.
- Identify major innovations in ancient China and their influence on the Chinese economy.

Key Vocabulary

artifact, beginning of Daoism, Black Sea, Buddhism, caravan, China, compass, Great Wall of China, Han dynasty, Laozi, markets, Mediterranean Sea, merchant, monopoly, Persian Gulf, Red Sea, seismograph, Siddhartha Gautama / Buddha, Silk Road, technology, trade, Zhou dynasty

Lesson Essential Question:

How did China become economically successful?

FLASHCARDS

1 ▸ Traveling the Silk Road

The Silk Road was a series of trade routes that connected China with markets in Europe, Central Asia, South Asia, North Africa, and the Middle East.

- The Silk Road was not a continuous road but rather a series of trade routes that connected China with Europe, India, the Middle East, and northern Africa.
- One of the main routes to the West extended about 4,000 miles.
- The sea routes of the Silk Road traveled via the South China Sea and the Indian Ocean to Iraq or Egypt. On the other side, merchants brought the goods to Alexandria, Egypt, and other places Europeans used for trade.

Why Does It Matter?

The Silk Road connected China with far-off lands. It was the first major trade system of its kind. Trade became a major part of the early Chinese economy.

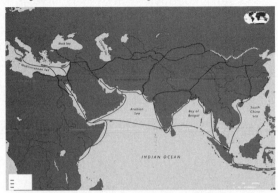

photo: Discovery Education
The Silk Road trade routes linked China to the West.

2 ▸ Trading Goods and Ideas

The Silk Road brought goods and ideas to China and gave China the opportunity to trade its goods with the outside world.

- The Chinese had a monopoly on silk. It was not made anywhere else in the world.
- China traded silk, porcelain, and other goods with merchants from other lands along the Silk Road.
- Merchants from other lands sold goods such as grapes, colored glass, and spices to China along the Silk Road.
- Merchants and travelers from different lands exchanged information and cultures.
- Monks and merchants from India brought Buddhism to China via the Silk Road.

Why Does It Matter?

The Silk Road brought people from many different cultures together to trade ideas and goods. China's monopoly on silk helped its economy thrive.

photo: Los Angeles County Museum of Art (www.lacma.org)
Buddhism was introduced via the Silk Road and would soon become an important religion in the country.

FLASHCARDS *(continued)*

3 **Early Achievements and Inventions**

The Shang, Zhou, and Han dynasties contributed new toolmaking technologies and other innovations to China.

- **People during the Shang dynasty learned how to make tools and other items out of bronze.**
- **Iron became an important part of the Chinese economy during the Zhou dynasty.**
- **Traditional Chinese medicine developed during the Han dynasty.**
- **The magnetic compass was invented during the Han dynasty.**
- **The seismograph was invented during the Han dynasty.**

Why Does It Matter?

The early Chinese developed new technologies and inventions that would influence later generations and the rest of the world. Today, many herbal remedies from Chinese medicine are used throughout the world, as are the magnetic compass and more advanced versions of the early seismograph.

The magnetic compass, invented during the Han dynasty, consisted of a large magnetic spoon on a bronze plate.

Name _____ **Date** _____

GRAPHIC ORGANIZER: Vocabulary Chart

Use the Vocabulary Chart to explore the meaning of the term *Silk Road*. For supporting resources, go to Regional Civilizations > Ancient China > Ancient Chinese Economy > Explore > Open for Business.

DEFINITION:	EXAMPLES (drawn or written):
Personal:	
Dictionary:	

TERM:
Silk Road

SENTENCES:		RELATED:	WORD PARTS:
Teacher/Book:			
Personal:			

Outside of School (Who would use the word? How would he or she use it?)

Name _____ Date _____

GRAPHIC ORGANIZER: Comparison Chart

Use this Comparison Chart to compare and contrast the contributions of the Shang, Zhou, and Han dynasties. For supporting resources, go to Regional Civilizations > Ancient China > Ancient Chinese Economy > Explore > Contributions of the Bronze Age.

Criteria	Years of Rule	Contributions	Innovations or Ideas Introduced by Other Cultures
Shang Dynasty			
Zhou Dynasty			
Han Dynasty			

© Discovery Education | www.DiscoveryEducation.com

Name _____ Date _____

EXPLORE: FOCUS QUESTIONS

Using what you learned from the Core Interactive Text, answer each page's focus question:

Open for Business

How did the ancient Chinese conduct trade with other civilizations?

_____

_____

_____

Contributions of the Bronze Age

What technological developments occurred during the Shang and Zhou dynasties?

_____

_____

_____

Origins of Traditional Chinese Healing

How did the Han contribute to traditional Chinese medicine?

_____

_____

_____

Finding True North

What other important innovations occurred during the Han dynasty?

_____

_____

_____

Chinese Goods

What kinds of goods did Chinese merchants trade?

_____

_____

_____

An Exchange of Cultures

How did Buddhism spread to China?

_____

_____

_____

PROJECTS AND ASSESSMENTS

Explain Activities

ACTIVITY TYPE: ENCYCLOPEDIA ENTRY

Ancient Chinese Economy

Write an encyclopedia entry describing a particular invention or innovation from ancient China. In the entry, you will identify what the invention or innovation did, why it was important, and how it contributed to the overall success of the Chinese economy.

ACTIVITY TYPE: YOU AS JOURNALIST

Ancient Chinese Economy

Imagine that you are a trader in ancient China and you have just come back from a trip along the Silk Road. Where did you go? What goods did you trade for? Write a story about your journey.

ACTIVITY TYPE: SOCIAL STUDIES EXPLANATION

Ancient Chinese Economy

In this Social Studies Explanation activity, you will use a template to assemble evidence from the sources you have explored. Then, you will write an answer to the Essential Question and defend your answer with supporting evidence.

Elaborate Activities

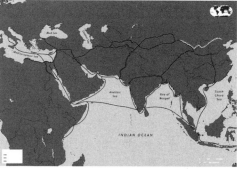

photo: Discovery Education

INVESTIGATION TYPE: TIMELINE INQUIRY

Ancient Chinese Economy

Discover the goods and ideas that flowed into and out of ancient China to create one of the greatest economies of the ancient world. What drove China's success?

PROJECTS AND ASSESSMENTS *(continued)*

photo: Los Angeles County Museum of Art (www.lacma.org)

ACTIVITY TYPE: CURRENT EVENTS CONNECTION

Ancient and Modern Trade

In this activity, you will compare the spread of ideas, technologies, and goods along the trade routes of ancient China with the use of the Internet in our modern world. Then, you will express your opinion in a brief report responding to the following question: How was the spread of goods, ideas, and technologies in ancient China similar to or different from how the Internet is used today?

photo: National Institutes of Health

ACTIVITY TYPE: ACT LOCALLY

Preventing Mosquito-Borne Disease

In this activity, you will study the most effective techniques and evaluate the best ways to implement them in your community. Then, you will propose a plan of action that can be used to help keep yourself and your community safer from mosquito-borne diseases.

photo: Los Angeles County Museum of Art (www.lacma.org)

ACTIVITY TYPE: CLASSROOM SPEECH

Sharing the Secret of Silk

In this activity, you will respond to the question of whether China should or should not have shared its secrets of silk making. Write your response in the form of either a persuasive open letter or a short persuasive speech.

Evaluate Activities

BRIEF-CONSTRUCTED RESPONSE (BCR)

Ancient Chinese Economy

EXTENDED-CONSTRUCTED RESPONSE (ECR)

Ancient Chinese Economy

UNIT 3: REGIONAL CIVILIZATIONS (2500 BCE TO 1054 CE)

Chapter 8: The Origins of Judaism

8.1 Culture and Beliefs of the Ancient Hebrews

photo: Getty Images

LESSON OVERVIEW

Lesson Objectives:

By the end of this lesson, you should be able to:

- Locate ancient Israel and its important cities and rivers on a historical map and a modern map.
- Describe the origins and characteristics of Judaism, the religion of the ancient Israelites.
- Identify important figures in Israelite (Hebrew) tradition (Abraham, Moses, Ruth, David).
- Analyze the role of women in Israelite society.
- Analyze the impact of the legal code of the ancient Israelites on surrounding civilizations and future traditions.

Key Vocabulary

Abraham, Assyrian Empire, Canaan, Christianity, code of law, Egypt, famine, founding of the kingdom of Israel, Hebrew Bible, Islam, Israel, Jerusalem, Jesus, Jordan River, Judaism, King David, King Solomon, Mediterranean Sea, monotheism, Moses, Muslims, pharaoh, polytheism, Red Sea, Ruth, Sabbath, Saul, slavery, Ten Commandments, Ur

Lesson Essential Question:

In what ways did the ancient Israelites influence religions and societies in ancient and modern times?

FLASHCARDS

1 ▸ The Land of Israel

The ancient Kingdom of Israel is located in the Middle East, in much the same area as the modern country.

- Israel is located west of the Mediterranean Sea.
- The Jordan River, an important source of water, flows along the eastern border of Israel and the West Bank.
- Jerusalem and Tel Aviv are the two most important cities in modern Israel

Why Does It Matter?

The land of Israel, and especially the city of Jerusalem, is considered holy by three major religions: Judaism, Christianity, and Islam.

photo: Library of Congress
This drawing shows a European artist's stylized interpretation of what Jerusalem may have looked like in the Middle Ages.

2 ▸ The Origins of Judaism

Judaism is the religion of the ancient Hebrew people. It is based on monotheism, the belief in a single god.

- Judaism is the religion of the ancient Israelite people. It is based on monotheism, the belief in a single God.
- Judaism derives its teachings from ancient texts. The texts provide laws believed to be given to the Jewish people by God.
- The Torah is the most important text in Judaism.
- According to the Torah, the patriarch Abraham founded Judaism when God called him to establish a new nation in Canaan, which would become Israel.
- The Ten Commandments are the best known laws of Judaism. They set forth a clear and simple moral code.

Why Does It Matter?

Judaism is the oldest monotheistic faith that is still practiced today. The belief in a single God who spoke to Abraham would become the basis for two other major religions, Christianity and Islam.

photo: Library of Congress
This image shows one possible location of Mount Sinai, the mountain where, according to the Torah, Moses received the Ten Commandments from God.

FLASHCARDS *(continued)*

3 ▸ Who's Who in the Torah

The Torah contains stories about many important people in the Hebrew tradition.

- Abraham was the first Hebrew to practice monotheism. Jews trace their lineage through his son Isaac.
- Moses, with God's help, led enslaved Israelites out of slavery in Egypt to the Promised Land.
- King David united the tribes of Israel and became one of its greatest kings.
- Ruth was a non-Israelite woman from Moab who was known for her strong loyalty to her Israelite mother-in law. She is considered the first convert to Judaism.

Why Does It Matter?

These biblical figures were key in establishing the religion and culture of ancient Israel. They have also influenced artists, writers, philosophers, and religious and political leaders throughout history.

photo: Library of Congress
Moses holds the Tablet of the Commandments.

4 ▸ Women in Ancient Israel

Early Hebrew society was patriarchal, or ruled by men. Women's roles were limited, but it was commanded that they be treated with respect.

- Like most ancient societies, early Israelite society was patriarchal, or ruled by men. Women's roles focused on the home. The Torah commanded that they be treated with respect.
- It was believed that a woman's most important task was to have and raise children.
- Jewish law focuses on the equality of all before the law, including women. This provided more legal protection than most ancient civilizations.
- Women did not choose their husbands or divorce them, but marriage required their consent in a formal, written contract.
- Women could not inherit property unless there were no male heirs.
- The marriage contract detailed financial support for women in the event of divorce or widowhood.
- Jewish law states that husbands must love and honor their wives.
- Women contributed to Jewish society and culture. Deborah was a judge who ruled Israel in the time before kings. Esther was a queen in Persia who saved many of her Jewish subjects from death.

Why Does It Matter?

The Israelite laws and customs about the treatment of women had a strong influence on Judaism to this day. In Israelite society, men and women did not sit together for prayer to minimize distraction. Traditionally observant Jews follow this law today.

photo: Bigstock
Jewish women were not allowed to pray with men in ancient Israel. Some Jews still follow this law today.

© Discovery Education | www.DiscoveryEducation.com

FLASHCARDS *(continued)*

5 Israelite Laws and Their Influence

Ancient Israel's society was based on the laws of the Torah, especially the Ten Commandments. Two other monotheistic faiths, Christianity and Islam arose out of Jewish tradition.

- **Christianity grew directly out of Judaism. Christians used the writings of the Torah as part of the Christian Bible.**
- **Many stories and laws familiar from the Hebrew Bible appear in Islam's sacred text, the Quran, interpreted from a new perspective.**
- **Jewish sacred texts are honored by Christians, who also revere the Ten Commandments.**
- **Jewish ritual also influenced some rituals of Islam related to dietary restrictions, daily prayer, fasting, and charity.**

Why Does It Matter?

The three monotheistic faiths, and the conflicts among them, would be a strong driving force in Western civilization and history.

photo: Library of Congress

Jerusalem is an important holy city in the Jewish, Christian, and Muslim religions.

Name _____ **Date** _____

GRAPHIC ORGANIZER: Summary Frames

Use these Summary Frames to summarize the founding of Judaism, the role of Moses in the Hebrew tradition, and the rise of the Kingdom of Israel. For supporting resources, go to Regional Civilizations > The Origins of Judaism > Culture and Beliefs of the Ancient Hebrews > Explore > The Roots of Judaism.

Name _____ **Date** _____

GRAPHIC ORGANIZER: Summary Frames *(continued)*

_____   _____   _____

_____   _____   _____

_____   _____   _____

Name _____ **Date** _____

GRAPHIC ORGANIZER: Comparison Chart

Use this Comparison Chart to compare and contrast the characteristics of Judaism, Christianity, and Islam. For supporting resources, go to Regional Civilizations > The Origins of Judaism > Culture and Beliefs of the Ancient Hebrews > Explore > Three Faiths.

Criteria	Founder	Beliefs	Characteristics of the Religion's Holy Book
Judaism			
Christianity			
Islam			

Name _____ Date _____

EXPLORE: FOCUS QUESTIONS

Using what you learned from the Core Interactive Text, answer each page's focus question:

Ancient Israel
Where is Israel located?

_____

_____

_____

The Roots of Judaism
What role did Abraham play in the culture of the ancient Hebrews?

_____

_____

_____

The Exodus
What role does Moses play in the Jewish tradition?

_____

_____

_____

A Culture of Law and Learning
How did the Torah impact the Jewish people?

_____

_____

_____

Becoming a Kingdom
How did the Kingdom of Israel rise?

_____

_____

_____

Name _____ Date _____

EXPLORE: FOCUS QUESTIONS *(continued)*

Women in Ancient Israel

What contributions did women make to early Israelite society?

_____

_____

_____

_____

Women of Valor

Which women made important contributions to Israelite and Jewish society?

_____

_____

_____

Three Faiths

How did Judaism impact other civilizations and religions?

_____

_____

_____

PROJECTS AND ASSESSMENTS

Explain Activities

ACTIVITY TYPE: DIAGRAM

Culture and Beliefs of the Ancient Hebrews

Choose one of the religions you have studied. Use the Venn diagram to compare and contrast the characteristics of Judaism with the characteristics of the religion you chose.

ACTIVITY TYPE: VISUALIZATION

Culture and Beliefs of the Ancient Hebrews

Think of some Torah stories that took place between the founding of Judaism and the time of King David. Choose one of these stories and draw pictures in the blank frames to retell the story.

ACTIVITY TYPE: SOCIAL STUDIES EXPLANATION

Culture and Beliefs of the Ancient Hebrews

In this Social Studies Explanation activity, you will use a template to assemble evidence from the sources you have explored. Then, you will write an answer to the Essential Question and defend your answer with supporting evidence.

Elaborate Activities

photo: Jupiterimages Corporation

ACTIVITY TYPE: SAY WHAT?

Moses's Farewell

Read an excerpt from Deuteronomy and translate it for modern times. Then, respond to the analysis questions.

PROJECTS AND ASSESSMENTS *(continued)*

photo: Getty Images

ACTIVITY TYPE: DOCUMENT-BASED INVESTIGATION

The Ancient Hebrews

How have the laws of the ancient Hebrews influenced laws and political philosophy throughout history? Research ancient Hebrew laws and philosophies. Use what you have learned to write a report and create a museum exhibit comparing ancient and modern laws.

Evaluate Activities

BRIEF-CONSTRUCTED RESPONSE (BCR)

The Ancient Hebrews

EXTENDED-CONSTRUCTED RESPONSE (ECR)

The Ancient Hebrews

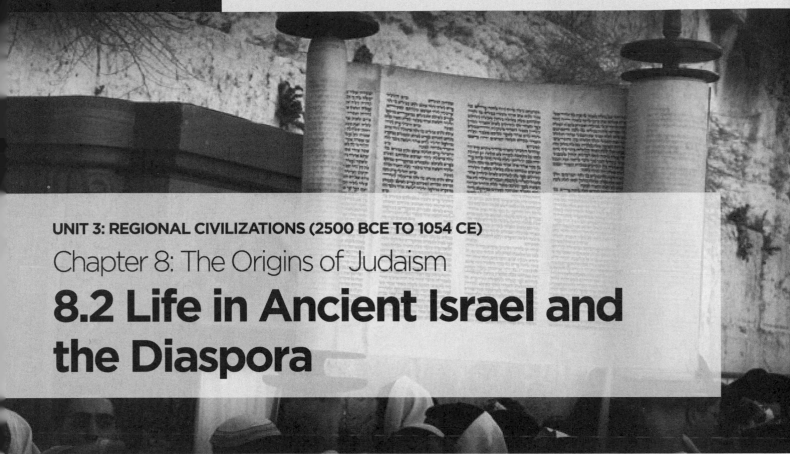

UNIT 3: REGIONAL CIVILIZATIONS (2500 BCE TO 1054 CE)

Chapter 8: The Origins of Judaism

8.2 Life in Ancient Israel and the Diaspora

photo: Getty Images

LESSON OVERVIEW

Lesson Objectives:

By the end of this lesson, you should be able to:

- Analyze the rites and rituals of Judaism.
- Compare the architectural features of the Jewish temple to other temples and houses of worship from ancient and modern times.
- Describe the different events that led to the formation of the various diasporas throughout the world.

Key Vocabulary

Alexander the Great, Assyrian Empire, Christianity, diaspora, Egypt, Hebrew Bible, Islam, Israel, Jerusalem, Judaism, Judea, King David, King Solomon, Mecca, Mesopotamia, monotheism, Muslims, Nebuchadnezzar, Neo-Babylonian Empire, rabbi, Roman Empire, Sabbath, Talmud, Ten Commandments, Torah

Lesson Essential Question:

How did ancient Judaism adapt and change with the diasporas of the Jewish people, and how did it influence other religions and peoples?

FLASHCARDS

1 Judaism: Its Rituals and Traditions

Judaism is the world's oldest monotheistic religion. Some of its rituals and traditions, as well as the architecture of its first temple, have influenced the other monotheistic religions, Christianity and Islam.

- **Jewish traditions such as the Sabbath and certain holidays continue today and have their parallels in other religions.**

- **The ancient Jewish temple in Jerusalem had its precedents in earlier religious architecture and included features that are present in modern synagogues, churches, and mosques.**

Why Does It Matter?

Though the Jews number just a fraction of 1 percent of the world's population today, their spiritual and moral innovations from ancient times have had an enormous influence on other religions.

photo: Library of Congress

What are the ancient origins of the symbols and rituals of Judaism?

2 The Diaspora

The ancient Israelite kingdom was conquered by a series of empires. Several times, the Jewish Temple was destroyed and Jews were forced to leave their religious and cultural center. However, they were able to maintain an identity by preserving and adapting their traditions.

- **After the death of King Solomon, the Israelite kingdom split into two states, Israel and Judah. Judah eventually gave its name to the religion of Judaism.**

- **Beginning in 721 BCE, a series of empires invaded the Israelite kingdoms. When the Israelites resisted, they were forced into exile.**

- **Judaism, based on the Torah, took form in exile and survived subsequent conquests and the dispersion of the people.**

- **Jewish religious traditions, including the study of the Torah and many rituals, continue today throughout the world.**

Why Does It Matter?

Despite the loss of their homeland, religious tradition and a sense of common history and identity kept Judaism alive through centuries of exile. The dispersion also helped to spread Judaism throughout the world and increased its influence on other faiths and cultures.

photo: IRC

The Second Temple was built upon the Jews' return to Jerusalem, expanded under the rule of King Herod, and eventually destroyed by the Romans after they conquered Jerusalem. This reconstruction is part of a large model of Jerusalem in around 50 CE in the Israel Museum in Jerusalem.

Name _____ **Date** _____

GRAPHIC ORGANIZER: Three-Way Venn Diagram

Use this Three-Way Venn Diagram to compare the three religions discussed in the text—Judaism, Christianity, and Islam. For supporting resources, go to Regional Civilizations > The Origins of Judaism > Life in Ancient Israel and the Diaspora > Explore > Keeping the Sabbath.

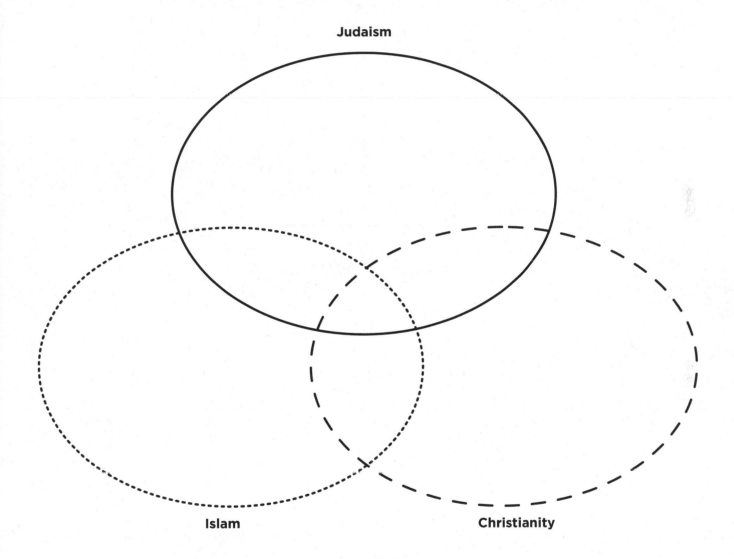

Judaism

Islam

Christianity

Name _____ Date _____

GRAPHIC ORGANIZER: Vocabulary Chart

Use this Vocabulary Chart to explore the definition of *diaspora*. For supporting resources, go to Regional Civilizations > The Origins of Judaism > Life in Ancient Israel and the Diaspora > Explore > A Common Identity, History, and Religion.

DEFINITION:

Personal:

Dictionary:

EXAMPLES (Drawn or Written):

TERM:
diaspora

SENTENCES:

Teacher/Book:

Personal:

RELATED:

WORD PARTS:

Outside of School (Who Would Use the Word? How Would He or She Use It?):

Name _____ Date _____

EXPLORE: FOCUS QUESTIONS

Using what you learned from the Core Interactive Text, answer each page's focus question:

Keeping the Sabbath
What are some of Judaism's important rites and rituals?

_____
_____
_____

Traditions and Celebrations
What traditions of the ancient Israelites have been adopted or adapted by other religions?

_____
_____
_____

The Temple of Solomon
How was the ancient Israelite temple constructed?

_____
_____
_____

Ancient Temple, Modern Echoes
How did the construction of the Jewish temple influence other religious architecture?

_____
_____
_____

A Kingdom Divided
What happened to the Israelite kingdom?

_____
_____
_____

Name _____ Date _____

EXPLORE: FOCUS QUESTIONS *(continued)*

The Persian, Roman, and Greek Empires Rule Judea
Why were the Jews eventually dispersed geographically?

_____
_____
_____
_____

A Common Identity, History, and Religion
What was the Diaspora of the Jews?

_____
_____
_____

PROJECTS AND ASSESSMENTS

Explain Activities

ACTIVITY TYPE: VISUALIZATION

Life in Ancient Israel and the Diaspora

In this Visualization activity, you will explore three of the events cited in the timeline on the page titled From Persia to Rome on the EXPLORE tab.

ACTIVITY TYPE: YOU AS JOURNALIST

The Fall of Jerusalem

In this activity, you will write (a) an on-the-scenes paragraph describing the fall of Jerusalem, and (b) a transcript of an interview between you as reporter and one of the three people listed.

ACTIVITY TYPE: SOCIAL STUDIES EXPLANATION

Life in Ancient Israel and the Diaspora

In this Social Studies Explanation activity, you will use a template to assemble evidence from the sources you have explored. Then, you will write an answer to the Essential Question and defend your answer with supporting evidence.

Elaborate Activities

photo: Getty Images

INVESTIGATION TYPE: TIMELINE MAP

Scattered to the Winds

What factors led to the scattering of the ancient Hebrew people out of Israel, and how did the Hebrew people affect the people and cultures that surrounded them? In this investigation, you will use the Timeline Map interactive tool to examine the political and cultural reasons behind the Diaspora of the Jewish people and to explore how the Hebrew people affected the different people and cultures they encountered.

PROJECTS AND ASSESSMENTS *(continued)*

photo: Getty Images

ACTIVITY TYPE: CURRENT EVENTS CONNECTION

Sons (and Daughters) of the Commandments

In this activity, you will research the ancient teachings that are the sources of Bar Mitzvah customs. Then, you will write a paragraph describing the ways in which modern-day Jews honor ancient teachings with this ceremony.

photo: Getty Images

ACTIVITY TYPE: SOCRATIC SEMINAR

The Wisdom of Hillel

In this activity, you will put Socrates's ideas to the test by completing a Socratic Seminar. You will analyze excerpts from the Talmud attributed to and concerning the ancient Jewish sage Rabbi Hillel. Then, you will debate whether Hillel's reputation for wisdom is justified and whether he merits being rated among history's wise teachers.

photo: Getty Images

ACTIVITY TYPE: DOCUMENT-BASED INVESTIGATION

A People's Survival

In this Document-Based Investigation, you will analyze and synthesize information from a variety of primary source documents to develop and defend an argument on the most important factor that contributed to the survival of Judaism from ancient times to today.

Evaluate Activities

BRIEF-CONSTRUCTED RESPONSE (BCR)

Life in Ancient Israel and the Diaspora

EXTENDED-CONSTRUCTED RESPONSE (ECR)

Life in Ancient Israel and the Diaspora

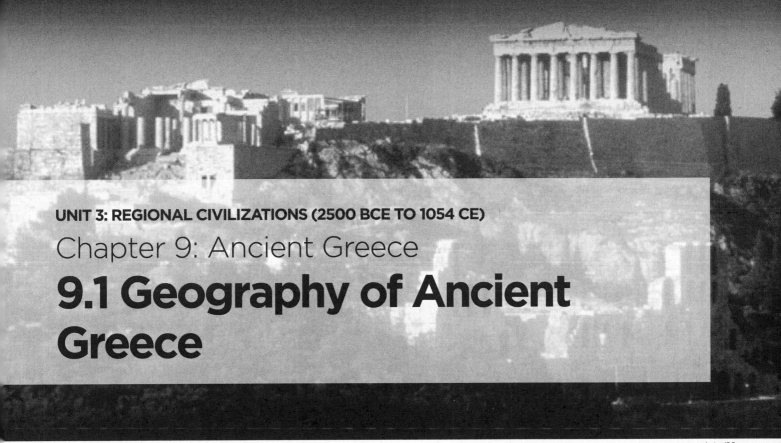

photo: IRC

UNIT 3: REGIONAL CIVILIZATIONS (2500 BCE TO 1054 CE)

Chapter 9: Ancient Greece

9.1 Geography of Ancient Greece

LESSON OVERVIEW

Lesson Objectives:

By the end of this lesson, you should be able to:

- Analyze the impact of Greek geography on the development of civilization in ancient Greece.
- Describe the origins of the Persian Empire and the relationship between Persia and Greece.
- Trace the major wars between Persia and Greek city-states.

Lesson Essential Question:

How did geography influence the development of Greek civilization?

Key Vocabulary

Acropolis, Aegean Sea, Aeneas, Anatolia, Athens, Attica, blockade, city-state, civilization, Constantinople, Crete, Cyrus/ Cyrus the Great, Darius, Europe, Greece, Greek Empire, Ionian Sea, island, King Xerxes, latitude, longitude, Macedonia, Marathon, Medes, Mediterranean Sea, Mount Olympus, Mycenae, Peloponnesus, peninsula, Persia, Persian Wars, Pompeii, Rhodes, Sparta, Thebes, Turkey

FLASHCARDS

1 Islands and Mountains

Ancient Greece had a very different geography from the river valley civilizations of Mesopotamia, India, China, and Egypt. As a result, it developed much differently as a civilization than the river valley civilizations.

- Ancient Greece was located in southeast Europe along the Mediterranean Sea.
- Ancient Greece was a series of mountainous islands and peninsulas. This affected the Greek way of life, including what crops people grew and how they traveled.
- The Mycenaeans controlled much of southern Greece from 1500 BCE to 1100 BCE. Their rule was followed by a period of chaos in Greece.
- Greek city-states developed after the Mycenaean period, with each city controlling the land around it. Greek geography made it difficult for city-states to expand their territory.
- Greek city-states developed in isolation from one another due to the geography of the region. The mountains, peninsulas, and islands forced each city to create its own identity, including government, military, and culture.
- Greek city-states established colonies along the Mediterranean and Black Sea coastlines.

Why Does It Matter?

Greece's many mountains and seas determined how Greek civilization developed. Greeks used the seas to develop a rich trade with other areas, while islands and mountains led to the development of city-states rather than a united civilization. These city-states would influence how future civilizations formed governments and studied the world around them.

photo: Pixabay

This image shows the ruins of Troy, a city captured by the Mycenaeans.

2 The Persian Empire

The Persian Empire was one of the largest empires in the ancient world. It covered parts of three continents: Europe, Africa, and Asia. The Persian Empire also introduced new ways of governing empires, which were used for centuries to come.

- bullet text Cyrus of Persia united the area that is present-day Iran under his rule and conquered neighboring areas, establishing the Persian Empire.
- His successors conquered more lands, until the Persian Empire stretched from Egypt to India.
- During their conquests, the Persians conquered several Greek colonies.
- King Darius I organized the empire so that the Persians could control the vast and diverse land they had conquered. He created a single currency, established satrapies, and built roads to link his empire together.

Why Does It Matter?

The Persian Empire was one of the largest ancient empires. Its control over Greek colonies would lead to decades of war between the two great powers.

photo: Pixabay

This image of Persian soldiers was taken from a relief at Persepolis.

FLASHCARDS *(continued)*

3 ⟩ The Persian Wars

The Persian Wars were fought between the Persian Empire and the Greek city-states between 500 BCE and 479 BCE. The wars determined whether the city-states would remain independent or become a part of the Persian Empire.

- Greek colonies in Turkey were conquered by the Persian Empire.
- These colonies rebelled against Persian rule in 500 BCE. Greek city-states from the Greek peninsula sent soldiers to help the colonies against the Persians. The Persians ultimately defeated the colonies and reestablished their power.
- In 490 BCE, King Darius sought to conquer the Greek peninsula. His troops were defeated at the Battle of Marathon.
- King Xerxes attempted to conquer Greece in 480 BCE. He won several victories and burned Athens to the ground. Finally, the Greek city-states won a sea victory at Salamis and a land victory at Plataea. Xerxes was defeated.

Why Does It Matter?

The Persian Wars united the Greek city-states together against a common Persian enemy. The mountains and islands of Greece made it difficult for the Persians to conquer all of the Greek city-states. The Greek victory ensured that Greece would remain independent from the Persian Empire.

photo: Getty Images Open Content Program

The illustrations on this Grecian urn commemorate the Persian Wars.

SOCIAL STUDIES TECHBOOK

Name _____ **Date** _____

GRAPHIC ORGANIZER: Cause/Effect Chart

Use this Cause/Effect chart to record information about how geography affected life in Ancient Greece. For supporting resources, go to Regional Civilizations > Ancient Greece > Geography of Ancient Greece > Explore > Islands and Mountains.

Cause   **Effect**

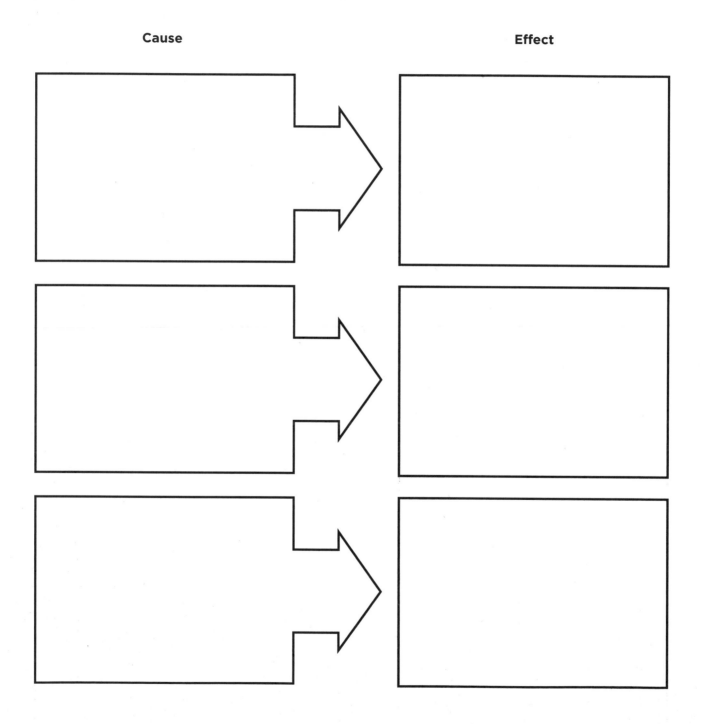

© Discovery Education | www.DiscoveryEducation.com

Name _____ **Date** _____

GRAPHIC ORGANIZER: Venn Diagram

Use this Venn Diagram to compare and contrast ancient Greece and the Persian Empire. For supporting resources, go to Regional Civilizations > Ancient Greece > Geography of Ancient Greece > Explore > The Persian Empire.

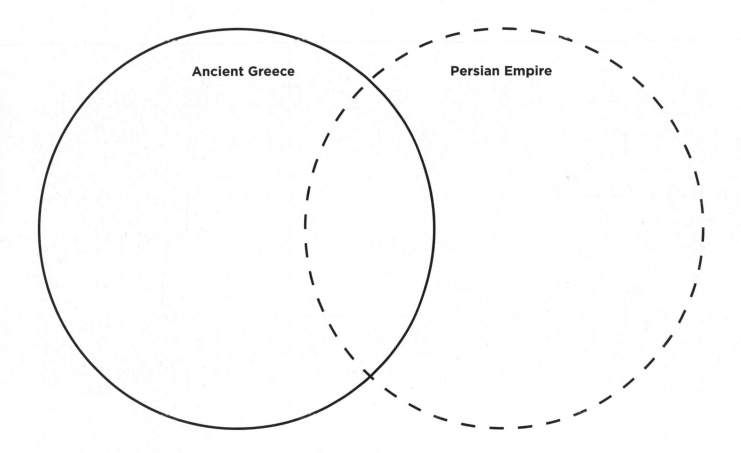

Ancient Greece   **Persian Empire**

Name _____ **Date** _____

 GRAPHIC ORGANIZER: Sequencing Chart

Use this Sequencing Chart to record information about the main events of the Persian Wars. For supporting resources, go to Regional Civilizations > Ancient Greece > Geography of Ancient Greece > Explore > Persia vs. Greece.

Event	Date	Summary

Name _____ **Date** _____

GRAPHIC ORGANIZER: Sequencing Chart *(continued)*

Event	Date	Summary

Name _____ Date _____

EXPLORE: FOCUS QUESTIONS

Using what you learned from the Core Interactive Text, answer each page's focus question:

Islands and Mountains

How did the geography of Greece influence its people?

_____
_____
_____

The Economy of Ancient Greece

How did the geography of Greece affect the development of its societies?

_____
_____
_____

Unique City-States

What were the other important cities in ancient Greece?

_____
_____
_____

The Persian Empire

How was the Persian Empire established?

_____
_____
_____

Persia vs. Greece

Why did tensions arise between Greece and Persia?

_____
_____
_____

Name _____   **Date** _____

EXPLORE: FOCUS QUESTIONS *(continued)*

The Persian Wars
What role did Greek geography play in the Persian Wars?

_____

_____

_____

The End of the Wars
How did the Persian Wars end?

_____

_____

_____

PROJECTS AND ASSESSMENTS

Explain Activities

ACTIVITY TYPE: ADVERTISEMENT

Geography of Ancient Greece

In this activity, you will create an advertisement that promotes the geographical features of Greece and shows how these features benefited the people of ancient Greece.

ACTIVITY TYPE: VISUALIZATION

Persian Wars Slide Show

In this Visualization activity, you will describe the major events of the Persian Wars that were fought between ancient Greece and the Persian Empire. Using the spaces provided, create drawings that show important events from the conflict. Then, write an informative caption for each drawing on the lines below each box.

ACTIVITY TYPE: SOCIAL STUDIES EXPLANATION

Geography of Ancient Greece

In this Social Studies Explanation activity, you will use a template to assemble evidence from the sources you have explored. Then, you will write an answer to the Essential Question and defend your answer with supporting evidence.

Elaborate Activities

photo: Getty Images

INVESTIGATION TYPE: MAP-GUIDED INQUIRY

Geography of Ancient Greece

How did geography influence the development of ancient Greek civilization? In this investigation, you will use the Map-Guided Inquiry interactive tool to examine how ancient Greece compares to modern Greece on a map.

PROJECTS AND ASSESSMENTS *(continued)*

photo: Pixabay

ACTIVITY TYPE: SAY WHAT?

Geography of Ancient Greece

The Greek author Herodotus wrote about the Persian Wars in "The History of Herodotus." In the excerpts given in this activity, Herodotus writes about how the geography of Greece played a role in the Battle of Thermopylae. Working with a partner, read one of the excerpts and translate it for modern times. Then, respond to the analysis questions.

photo: Pixabay

ACTIVITY TYPE: DOCUMENT-BASED INVESTIGATION

The Impact of Greece's Location

Did the negative aspects of ancient Greece's sea-based location outweigh the positive aspects? In this activity, you will write a statement for a debate or an editorial for an imaginary ancient Greek newspaper, stating your position and providing evidence to support your ideas.

Evaluate Activities

BRIEF-CONSTRUCTED RESPONSE (BCR)

Geography of Ancient Greece

EXTENDED-CONSTRUCTED RESPONSE (ECR)

Geography of Ancient Greece

UNIT 3: REGIONAL CIVILIZATIONS (2500 BCE TO 1054 CE)

Chapter 9: Ancient Greece
9.2 Greek Political Systems

LESSON OVERVIEW

Lesson Objectives:

By the end of this lesson, you should be able to:

- Trace the roots of changes in governments from monarchy to aristocracy to oligarchy in ancient Greek city-states.
- Describe the political structures in ancient Greece—particularly Athens—and compare the democratic concepts developed in the region (city-state, constitutions, lawmaking bodies) to modern democracy.
- Compare and contrast the characteristics of the Greek city-states of Athens and Sparta.

Key Vocabulary

Alexander the Great, Alexander's Empire, aristocracy, Athens, citizen, city-state, constitution, democracy, direct democracy, Ethiopia, Greece, hierarchy, imperialism, monarchy, nationalism, oligarchy, Peloponnesian Wars, Peloponnesus, Persian Wars, polis, popular sovereignty, representative democracy, representative government, Sparta

Lesson Essential Question:

To what extent were ancient Greek political systems democratic?

FLASHCARDS

1 Experimenting with Government

Greek city-states tried many different types of government. Some settled quickly on a form of government such as a monarchy or an oligarchy. Athenian government developed slowly, through a series of reforms, into a new type of political system: the democracy.

- Many Greek city-states started out as monarchies. Some became aristocracies or oligarchies when the aristocrats close to the king overthrew the monarch and took power.
- When the commoners became discontented with oligarchies, they supported strongmen who overthrew the oligarchies and established themselves as tyrants. Some tyrants were very popular and helped their city-states prosper. Other tyrants abused their power and became unpopular.

Why Does It Matter?

Greek city-states were ruled by different types of governments. Each type of government had advantages and disadvantages. The Greek city-states were shaped by their differing approaches to government.

photo: Getty's Open Content Program

Periander, the tyrant of the city-state of Corinth, brought prosperity to Corinth during his rule. Many tyrants were popular among those they ruled because they instituted programs that helped common people and brought prosperity to their city-states.

2 Athenian Democracy

Athenian democracy was somewhat different from modern democracies, but its principles are still seen today in governments around the world.

- Athenians took gradual steps to expand access to government for common people until all Athenian citizens could participate in government.
- In Athens, all citizens had a voice and a vote in the making of laws. Citizens also served on juries and could run for public office.
- Athenian democracy was a direct democracy, which meant that all citizens had a direct role in the making of laws and the running of the government.
- Citizens were free male adults whose parents were born in Athens. Women were not allowed to participate in government.
- Residents of Athens who did not have Athenian parents, or who were enslaved, could not become citizens or participate in government, either.

Why Does It Matter?

Athens was the first democracy. It served as one of the inspirations for the founders of the U.S. government more than 2,000 years later.

photo: Library of Congress

The Agora of ancient Athens was the main meeting place of the city. It was the site of the market and a large library, and as such was the economic and cultural hub of Athens.

FLASHCARDS *(continued)*

3 Athens and Sparta

Athens and Sparta were two of the most powerful Greek city-states. They developed into very different societies. Their governments, economies, and cultures were almost complete opposites. They were constant rivals.

- Athens built its economy on trade. It depended heavily on the resources and wealth it received from its trade network.

- Because of its wealth from trade, Athens was able to become a culturally rich city-state. Athenians sculpted, made pottery, wrote plays and poetry, and composed music. They debated ideas. Athenian boys were trained to become thinkers as well as artisans or merchants.

- Sparta developed as a farming and militaristic city-state. Enslaved people called helots grew food on the rich soil around Sparta, while Spartan citizens trained as warriors to defend their city-state from attacks and uprisings. Spartan boys were trained from birth to become warriors, and even women received some training in military tactics.

- Athens and Sparta, along with their allies, fought the Peloponnesian War from 431 BCE to 404 BCE. After a long siege in 404 BCE, Sparta conquered Athens, destroying its walls and its control over ancient Greece.

Why Does It Matter?

Sparta and Athens offered two very different models of how a city-state could function. Although Sparta triumphed over Athens in the Peloponnesian War, Athens's legacy has been greater. The influence of Athenian culture and ideas can still be felt today.

photo: Getty's Open Content Program

This vase shows the Peloponnesian War that divided ancient Greece between Athenian and Spartan allies.

Greek Political Systems

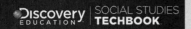

Name ______________________________ **Date** ______________

GRAPHIC ORGANIZER: Comparison Chart

Use this Comparison Chart to compare four forms of government. For supporting resources, go to Regional Civilizations > Ancient Greece > Greek Political Systems > Explore > Early Forms of Greek Government.

Criteria	Monarchy	Oligarchy	Tyranny	Democracy
Head of State				
Who Are the Decision Makers?				
How Is Power Acquired?				
How Much Power Do the People Have?				
How Are Political Freedoms Determined?				

Name _____ **Date** _____

GRAPHIC ORGANIZER: Comparison Chart

Use this Comparison Chart to compare the city-states of Athens and Sparta. For supporting resources, go to Regional Civilizations > Ancient Greece > Greek Political Systems > Explore > Ancient Greek Democracy.

Criteria	Athens	Sparta
Location in Greece		
Style of Government		
Culture		
Societal Rules		
Education		

Name _____   Date _____

EXPLORE: FOCUS QUESTIONS

Using what you learned from the Core Interactive Text, answer each page's focus question:

Early Forms of Greek Government
Who ruled the first city-states?

_____

_____

_____

The Beginnings of Democracy
How did ancient Greek democracies develop?

_____

_____

_____

Ancient Greek Democracy
How did Greek democracy work?

_____

_____

_____

Life in Athens
What made Athens powerful? What was daily life like in Athens?

_____

_____

_____

Sparta: A Military Oligarchy
How were the governments of Athens and Sparta different?

_____

_____

_____

Name _____ Date _____

EXPLORE: FOCUS QUESTIONS *(continued)*

Life in Ancient Sparta
What was daily life like in ancient Sparta?

_____
_____
_____
_____

Tensions between Athens and Sparta
How did war Between Athens and Sparta affect Greek government?

_____
_____
_____

PROJECTS AND ASSESSMENTS

Explain Activities

ACTIVITY TYPE: DIAGRAM

Greek Political Systems

In this activity, you will use a Comparison Chart to take notes on the similarities and differences between the governments of ancient Athens and the United States.

ACTIVITY TYPE: QUICK WRITE

Greek Political Systems

In this Quick Write activity, you will choose to focus on either ancient Athens or ancient Sparta. Classify your chosen city-state's government and provide three pieces of evidence to support your classification.

ACTIVITY TYPE: SOCIAL STUDIES EXPLANATION

Greek Political Systems

In this Social Studies Explanation activity, you will use a template to assemble evidence from the sources you have explored. Then, you will write an answer to the Essential Question and defend your answer with supporting evidence.

Elaborate Activities

photo: Discovery Education

INVESTIGATION TYPE: HISTORICAL PERSPECTIVES

Greek Society

Your mission is to get to know four individuals from ancient Greek society and explore the perspectives each would have on key issues of the day.

photo: Getty's Open Content Program

ACTIVITY TYPE: ROLE PLAY

Inside the Life of an Ancient Greek

In this activity, you will imagine that you live in either ancient Athens or ancient Sparta. Write a journal entry describing your experiences as one of the following residents of your chosen city-state: a citizen, a woman, a worker without citizen status (a non-citizen), or a slave. Your entry should focus on how your ability (or lack of ability) to participate in government affects your life.

PROJECTS AND ASSESSMENTS *(continued)*

photo: Jupiterimages Corporation

ACTIVITY TYPE: SAY WHAT?

The Roots of the U.S. Constitution

In this activity, you will be assigned a portion of the U.S. Constitution to read and translate for modern times. Then, you will respond to the analysis questions.

photo: Pixabay

ACTIVITY TYPE: DOCUMENT-BASED INVESTIGATION

For the People, by the People?

In this activity, you will write an op-ed article for a modern-day newspaper explaining how the ancient Athenian government worked. Then, you will write interview questions and responses, from an ancient Athenian's perspective, on the effectiveness of the government.

Evaluate Activities

BRIEF-CONSTRUCTED RESPONSE (BCR)

Greek Political Systems

EXTENDED-CONSTRUCTED RESPONSE (ECR)

Greek Political Systems

UNIT 3: REGIONAL CIVILIZATIONS (2500 BCE TO 1054 CE)

Chapter 9: Ancient Greece

9.3 Greek Cultural Achievements

LESSON OVERVIEW

Lesson Objectives:

By the end of this lesson, you should be able to:

- **Describe the philosophical ideas of Socrates, Plato, and Aristotle. Connect their philosophies to current ideas of governance and compare them to other ancient political philosophies.**

- **Identify important achievements and contributions (e.g., mythology, democracy, athletic competitions) of ancient Greeks that persist to the modern era. Connect these cultural features with elements of Greek political society.**

- **Trace Alexander the Great's conquests and the cultural diffusion of Hellenistic traditions.**

Key Vocabulary

Acropolis, agora, Alexander the Great, Alexander's Empire, Alexandria, aristocracy, Aristotle, city-state, constitutional monarchy, cultural diffusion, democracy, epic, Hellenistic Age, Macedonia, monarchy, mythology, oligarchy, Parthenon, philosophy, Plato, Socrates, Socratic method, stela

Lesson Essential Question:

How has classical Greek culture affected our modern lives?

FLASHCARDS

1 ▸ The Ideas of Socrates, Plato, and Aristotle

Socrates, Plato, and Aristotle each developed distinctive philosophies that had similarities and differences with other philosophies.

- Socrates used a method of teaching called the Socratic method.
- Socrates stressed the pursuit of morality.
- Plato wrote down the ideas of Socrates in a series of books called dialogues.
- Plato believed there was an ideal form of all objects and ideas that was beyond the five senses.
- Plato wrote the *Republic*, which describes his version of an ideal society and influenced many thinkers throughout history.
- The ideas in the *Republic* contradicted the ideas of other ancient philosophies.
- Aristotle analyzed the process of logical thinking.
- Aristotle believed that in the real world a constitutional monarchy was the best form of government.

Why Does It Matter?

The philosophies of Socrates, Plato, and Aristotle greatly influenced political and cultural life in ancient Greece. These philosophies were passed on through the ages and influenced leaders throughout Western history.

photo: Getty Images
During the Middle Ages in Europe, Christian, Jewish, and Arab scholars admired the writings of Aristotle.

2 ▸ Important Achievements of the Ancient Greeks

The ancient Greeks were responsible for many cultural achievements that influenced societies around them as well as future civilizations.

- The ancient Greeks developed the first version of democracy.
- The ancient Greeks developed a complex mythology that influenced Roman mythology.
- The Olympic Games began in ancient Greece as part of a religious festival.
- The Greek language forms the basis of many English words.
- Homer wrote the epic poems the *Iliad* and the *Odyssey*.
- Greek drama included comedy and tragedy.
- Sophocles wrote many great tragedies, including *Oedipus Rex*.

Why Does It Matter?

Greek democracy had a strong effect on the formation of later democracies, including the United States. Greek mythology still influences modern culture. The Olympic Games are today among the largest international sporting events in the world. The works of the ancient Greek writers are depicted through books, theater, and film in today's world.

photo: Bigstock
The ancient Greeks dedicated the temple called the Parthenon, located in Athens, to the goddess Athena.

FLASHCARDS *(continued)*

3 ▸ The Conquests and Impact of Alexander the Great

Alexander the Great conquered the Persian Empire and spread Greek ideas and culture.

- Alexander the Great won a series of victories over the Persian army and thereby gained control of the Persian Empire.
- Alexander promoted interactions between the Macedonians and the Persians.
- The conquests of Alexander spread Greek ideas and culture throughout the lands he conquered in Asia.
- The conquests of Alexander caused Greek and Asian cultures to mix, thereby producing the Hellenistic Age.

Why Does It Matter?

The mixing of Greek and Asian cultures caused by Alexander's conquest produced the Hellenistic Age. During this period, scientists and artists created great works that still affect our lives.

photo: Bigstock

After conquering the Persian Empire, Alexander adopted the Persian custom of viewing the king as a godlike ruler. Many Macedonian troops disliked this change because they viewed Alexander as a fellow warrior.

Name _____ Date _____

GRAPHIC ORGANIZER: Three-Way Venn Diagram

Use this Three-Way Venn Diagram to compare and contrast the philosophies of Socrates, Plato, and Aristotle. For supporting resources, go to Regional Civilizations > Ancient Greece > Greek Cultural Achievements > Explore > Socrates.

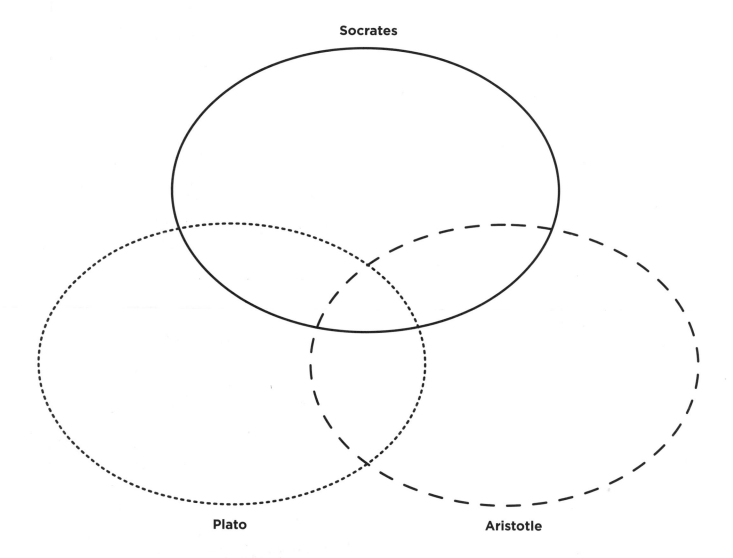

Name _____ Date _____

GRAPHIC ORGANIZER: GREASES Chart

Use this GREASES Chart to summarize the achievements and impact of ancient Greek culture. For supporting resources, go to Regional Civilizations > Ancient Greece > Greek Cultural Achievements > Explore > Art and Architecture.

Government	
Religion	
Economic	
Art & Architecture	
Science & Technology	
Environment	
Social & Cultural Values	

Name _____ **Date** _____

GRAPHIC ORGANIZER: Summary Frames

Use these Summary Frames to chart the major events in the expansion of Hellenistic Greece. For supporting resources, go to Regional Civilizations > Ancient Greece > Greek Cultural Achievements > Explore > Alexander the Great.

_____   _____   _____

_____   _____   _____

_____   _____   _____

_____   _____   _____

_____   _____   _____

_____   _____   _____

Name _____ **Date** _____

GRAPHIC ORGANIZER: Summary Frames *(continued)*

_____   _____   _____

_____   _____   _____

_____   _____   _____

Name _____ Date _____

EXPLORE: FOCUS QUESTIONS

Using what you learned from the Core Interactive Text, answer each page's focus question:

The Golden Age of Greece

What were the major cultural innovations of ancient Greece?

_____
_____
_____
_____

Socrates

What were the ideas of Socrates and how did they influence the world?

_____
_____
_____
_____

Plato

What were the ideas of Plato?

_____
_____
_____
_____

The Republic

What is the importance of *The Republic*?

_____
_____
_____
_____

Aristotle

What were the ideas of Aristotle?

_____
_____
_____
_____

Math and Science

How did ancient Greek math and science influence modern life?

_____
_____
_____
_____

Name _____ Date _____

EXPLORE: FOCUS QUESTIONS *(continued)*

Art and Architecture
What was the cultural influence of ancient Greece?

_____

_____

_____

Religion in Ancient Greece
What type of religion did the ancient Greeks practice?

_____

_____

_____

The Olympics
What were the Olympics?

_____

_____

_____

Language and Literature in Ancient Greece
What other cultural contributions did the ancient Greeks make?

_____

_____

_____

Alexander the Great
How did Alexander the Great form an empire?

_____

_____

_____

The Cultural Impact of Alexander the Great
How did the conquests of Alexander the Great influence the cultures of Asia and Greece?

_____

_____

_____

PROJECTS AND ASSESSMENTS

Explain Activities

ACTIVITY TYPE: DIAGRAM

Greek Cultural Achievements

Use at least 12 words from the Word Bank to create a graphic response to the Essential Question. You may add any other words or symbols, but you must use all of the starred words from the Word Bank. Summarize your map at the bottom and be prepared to present your thinking.

ACTIVITY TYPE: DIAGRAM

Greek Cultural Achievements

Use the graphic organizer to take notes on the similarities and differences between Plato's political system and the political system of another culture you have studied.

ACTIVITY TYPE: SOCIAL STUDIES EXPLANATION

Greek Cultural Achievements

In this Social Studies Explanation activity, you will use a template to assemble evidence from the sources you have explored. Then, you will write an answer to the Essential Question and defend your answer with supporting evidence.

Elaborate Activities

photo: Getty Images

INVESTIGATION TYPE: SOURCE ANALYSIS

The Temple of Apollo at Delphi

What can we learn about Ancient Greek society and culture from studying the ruins of the Temple of Apollo? Your mission is to explore images of an ancient Greek temple to learn more about Greek society.

photo: Getty Images

ACTIVITY TYPE: PITCH YOUR IDEA

Bid for Acropolis Construction

In this activity, you will have the choice of working as an engineer or a mathematician. You will write a multistep presentation that explains your work and how it sets you apart from others.

PROJECTS AND ASSESSMENTS *(continued)*

photo: Dreamstime

ACTIVITY TYPE: YOU AS ARTIST

Modern Greek Myth

In this activity, you will recount a modern event that you have observed or that you know about by creating a Greek myth that describes or explains what happens during the event. This myth should involve Greek gods and goddesses.

photo: Jupiterimages Corporation

ACTIVITY TYPE: DOCUMENT-BASED INVESTIGATION

Influencing Our Culture

How have the architecture and literature of ancient Greece influenced modern culture? Which Greek cultural contribution, architecture or literature, has influenced modern culture more? In this activity, you will answer these questions in the form of either a report or a slideshow.

Evaluate Activities

BRIEF-CONSTRUCTED RESPONSE (BCR)

Greek Cultural Achievements

EXTENDED-CONSTRUCTED RESPONSE (ECR)

Greek Cultural Achievements

UNIT 3: REGIONAL CIVILIZATIONS (2500 BCE TO 1054 CE)

Chapter 10: The Roman Republic and Empire

10.1 Geography and Economy of Ancient Rome

photo: Getty Images

LESSON OVERVIEW

Lesson Objectives:

By the end of this lesson, you should be able to:

- **Locate ancient Rome and its important cities and rivers on a historical and a modern map.**
- **Connect ancient Rome's location and its expansion through conquest and trade.**
- **Analyze the impact of coined money and roads on trade inside the Roman Empire.**

Key Vocabulary

Aachen, agriculture, Alps, Apennine Mountains, barter, climate, climate region, ecosystem, empire, Forum, Gaul, George Washington, Great Britain, Italy, latitude, Latium, longitude, markets, Mediterranean Sea, North Africa, peninsula, Remus, Roman Empire, Rome, Romulus, Spain, Tiber River

Lesson Essential Question:

How did geography and trade routes impact the growth of Rome?

FLASHCARDS

1 Where Was Rome?

Rome grew from a city in central Italy to a huge empire that occupied parts of Europe, Africa, and Asia all at once.

- Rome was founded on the Tiber River, in the center of the Italian peninsula.
- The Roman Empire expanded as far north as modern-day Great Britain and Scotland.
- The empire expanded as far southwest as the country of Morocco and as far east as the country of Syria.

Why Does It Matter?

The location of Rome led to the success of the city and its eventual expansion into an empire. Rome's large size meant that it had a significant influence through its military, trade, and culture.

photo: Corbis
The Roman Empire began as a small city in central Italy but expanded greatly over hundreds of years.

2 Location Leads to Expansion

Rome's location and geography gave it advantages that other locations did not have.

- Rome's location on the Tiber River in central Italy meant that Roman traders could easily sail the Mediterranean to trade with other places.
- The mountains and hills of Italy helped keep Romans safe from invasions.
- Rome's warm climate meant that it was a good location for farming, which meant that Romans had a plentiful food supply.

Why Does It Matter?

Rome's geographic conditions helped it to develop a trade-based economy and made it easier for Rome to expand throughout the Mediterranean region.

photo: Library of Congress
Rome's location and climate made it an excellent location for growing grains and other crops.

FLASHCARDS *(continued)*

3 ▶ Roman Roads and Coins

Roman coins and roads helped make trade and travel much easier during the Roman Empire.

- Romans built thousands of miles of roads and bridges that were used by soldiers, messengers, and traders throughout the empire.
- Romans had such advanced engineering technology that some of their roads still exist today.
- Romans minted coins that were used for trade throughout the empire and showed images of Roman rulers, gods, and goddesses.

Why Does It Matter?

Accomplishments such as roads, bridges, and coins helped Romans develop trade networks that allowed them to prosper and helped unify the empire.

photo: Library of Congress

The development of roads made travel and trade throughout the empire easier. This helped Rome expand its influence and empire.

Name _____ Date _____

GRAPHIC ORGANIZER: Main Idea Web

Use this Main Idea Web to organize details about the geography of Rome. For supporting resources, go to Regional Civilizations > The Roman Republic and Empire > Geography and Economy of Ancient Rome > Explore > The Founding of Rome.

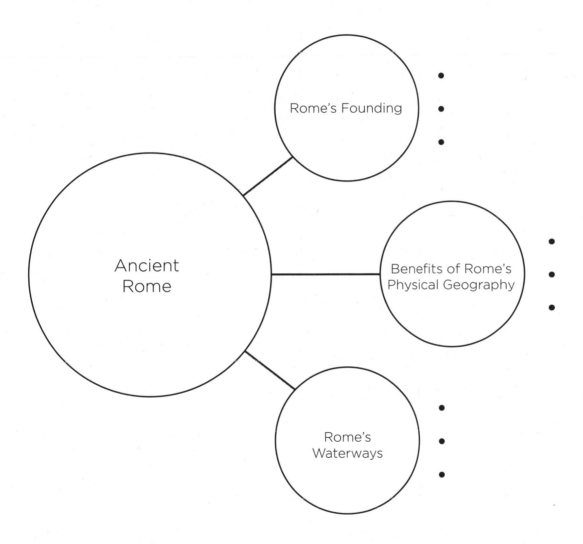

Name _____ **Date** _____

GRAPHIC ORGANIZER: Problem/Solution Chart

Use this Problem/Solution Chart to describe the challenges that Rome faced as it expanded its territory (problems) and the ways in which Roman citizens met those challenges (solutions). For supporting resources, go to Regional Civilizations > The Roman Republic and Empire > Geography and Economy of Ancient Rome > Explore > Roman Roads and Bridges.

Problem   **Solution**

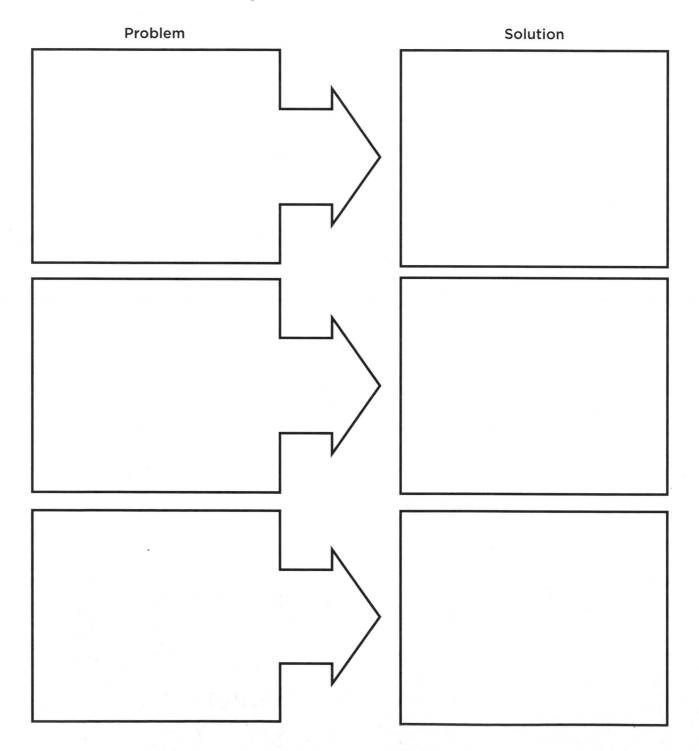

Name _____ Date _____

GRAPHIC ORGANIZER: Problem/Solution Chart *(continued)*

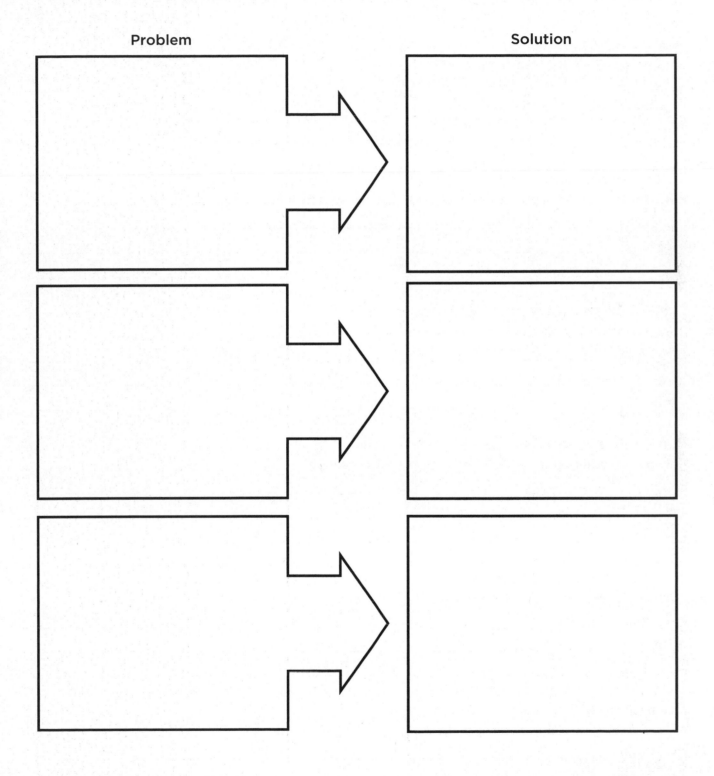

Problem   Solution

Name _____ Date _____

EXPLORE: FOCUS QUESTIONS

Using what you learned from the Core Interactive Text, answer each page's focus question:

The Founding of Rome

Where was ancient Rome?

_____
_____
_____
_____

Natural Benefits

What benefits did Rome's location provide the city and its inhabitants?

_____
_____
_____
_____

The Importance of Rome's Waterways

How did Rome's geography help it to prosper?

_____
_____
_____
_____

Roman Roads and Bridges

How did Roman roads and bridges impact the economy?

_____
_____
_____
_____

Rome's Monetary System

What effect did the Roman monetary system have on Rome's economy?

_____
_____
_____
_____

The History of Money

What is the cultural and historical significance of Roman coins?

_____
_____
_____
_____

PROJECTS AND ASSESSMENTS

Explain Activities

ACTIVITY TYPE: DIAGRAM

Geography and Economy of Rome

Use at least 10 words from the Word Bank to create a graphic response to the Essential Question.

ACTIVITY TYPE: ADVERTISEMENT

Roman Innovations

In this activity, you will create an advertisement for a company that has created a new innovation related to Roman roads or coins.

ACTIVITY TYPE: SOCIAL STUDIES EXPLANATION

Geography and Economy of Ancient Rome

In this Social Studies Explanation activity, you will use a template to assemble evidence from the sources you have explored. Then, you will write an answer to the Essential Question and defend your answer with supporting evidence.

Elaborate Activities

photo: Getty Images

INVESTIGATION TYPE: DATA ANALYSIS

Transportation and Trade in Ancient Rome

Your mission is to analyze the methods of transportation and trade routes used by the Romans as their empire expanded to the edges of the known world.

photo: Library of Congress

ACTIVITY TYPE: SAY WHAT?

Rome and Its Surroundings

In this activity, you will read one excerpt from either Strabo's "Geographica" or Titus Livius's "The History of Rome" and translate it for modern times.

PROJECTS AND ASSESSMENTS *(continued)*

photo: Getty Images

ACTIVITY TYPE: CURRENT EVENTS CONNECTION

Unification, Past and Present

In this activity, you will research how both the Roman Empire and the European Union used travel, trade, and currency to achieve unification. You will then write a speech to be given to a future world organization comparing the two unions and explaining which was more successful and why.

photo: Discovery Education

ACTIVITY TYPE: DOCUMENT-BASED INVESTIGATION

Rome: Geography and Economy

As the Roman Empire grew and spread through the Mediterranean and across Europe and parts of Asia, the culture of Rome diffused across the conquered territories. Military conquest, technological advancements, and trade relationships all helped foster this diffusion. In this Document-Based Investigation, you will analyze source materials and investigate this question: How did trade help spread Roman ways of life throughout the empire?

Evaluate Activities

BRIEF-CONSTRUCTED RESPONSE (BCR)

Geography and Economy of Ancient Rome

EXTENDED-CONSTRUCTED RESPONSE (ECR)

Geography and Economy of Ancient Rome

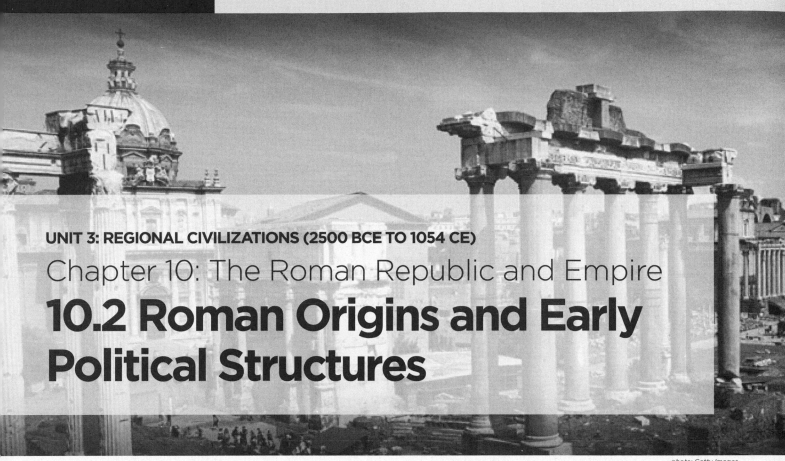

UNIT 3: REGIONAL CIVILIZATIONS (2500 BCE TO 1054 CE)

Chapter 10: The Roman Republic and Empire

10.2 Roman Origins and Early Political Structures

photo: Getty Images

LESSON OVERVIEW

Lesson Objectives:

By the end of this lesson, you should be able to:

- Trace the roots of Roman civilization to the contributions of Etruscans and Greek colonists.
- Analyze the political structure in ancient Rome and the democratic concepts developed in the region (separation of powers, representative government); compare to the democracies of Athens and of modern states.
- Describe the role of the Punic Wars in the growth of the Roman Empire.

Lesson Essential Question:

Was the Roman Republic democratic?

Key Vocabulary

Aeneas, Alps, assembly, bicameral, Carthage, census, Cincinnatus, citizen, code of law, Commodus, Constantine, consul, democracy, dictator, Diocletian, Emperor Augustus, Etruscans, Europe, Forum, Gaul, gladiator, Goths, Hannibal, Italy, Julius Caesar, jury, Latium, Mediterranean Sea, Octavian, oligarchy, Pantheon, patrician, peninsula, plebian, Punic Wars, Remus, representative, representative government, republic, Roman Empire, Roman Republic, Roman Senate, Rome, Romulus, Senate, Sicily, slavery, slaves, social class, Spain, Tiber River, tribune, Twelve Tables, Zama

FLASHCARDS

1 ▸ Rome's Early Influences

The early city of Rome was greatly influenced by the ancient Greek and Etruscan cultures.

- **According to the Roman legends, Rome was founded by descendants of the Trojan hero Aeneas.**
- **Rome was ruled by Etruscan kings, who had overthrown the Latin kings.**
- **The Romans may have adopted the Etruscan alphabet, Etruscan and Greek gods, and Greek political philosophy.**

Why Does It Matter?

The cultures that influenced Rome in its early history helped create Roman political philosophy and society, which have influenced many modern cultures.

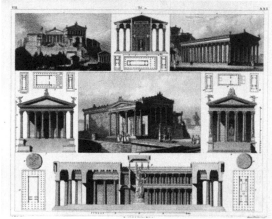

photo: Library of Congress

Greeks, Etruscans, and Latins all contributed to Roman ideas and culture.

2 ▸ The Roman Republic

The Roman Republic was a government in which the people elected their leaders. Roman citizens had certain rights and responsibilities.

- **Patricians had most of the power at first, but over time plebeians fought for and won a significant role in their government.**
- **Rome's government was made up of three parts. Each had the ability to limit the power of the other parts.**
- **Romans created a written code of laws to ensure that people were treated fairly.**

Why Does It Matter?

Many of the structures and principles of the Roman Republic influenced the creation of later democracies, including the United States.

photo: Library of Congress

The Romans created a republic and structured the government so that no one person or group could gain too much power.

FLASHCARDS *(continued)*

3 The Punic Wars

Between 264 and 146 BCE, Rome fought three wars, known as the Punic Wars, against the powerful city of Carthage.

- **In the first Punic War, Rome built up its army and gained the island of Sicily, as well as power in the Mediterranean Sea.**
- **In the second Punic War, the brilliant Carthaginian leader Hannibal almost captured Rome, but was eventually defeated by the Roman general Scipio.**
- **In the last Punic War, Rome defeated and destroyed Carthage.**

Why Does It Matter?

Through the Punic Wars, Rome gained power over the Mediterranean and a large amount of territory in North Africa and southern Europe. This expansion began the spread of the Roman Empire.

photo: From The New York Public Library

Between 264 BCE and 146 BCE, Rome fought three wars against Carthage and eventually gained control of all of the territory that had belonged to the North African power.

Name _____ **Date** _____

GRAPHIC ORGANIZER: Main Idea Web

Use this Main Idea Web to record information about early Roman history. For supporting resources, go to Regional Civilizations > The Roman Republic and Empire > Roman Origins and Early Political Structures > Explore > The Roots of Roman Civilization.

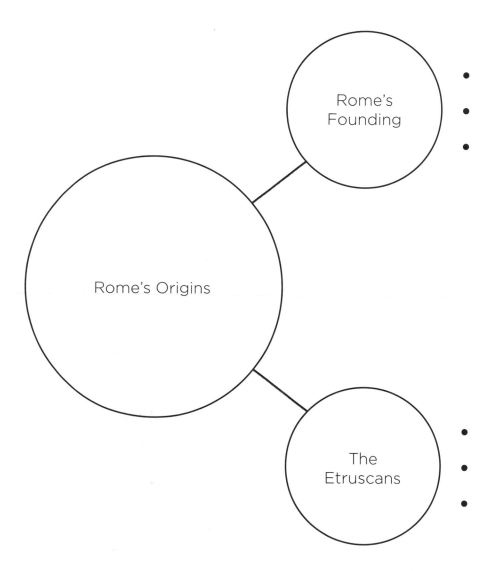

Discovery SOCIAL STUDIES
EDUCATION **TECHBOOK**

Name _____ Date _____

GRAPHIC ORGANIZER: Cause/Event/Effect Chart

Use this Cause/Event/Effect Chart to record the causes that led to the creation of the Roman Republic and the effects the republic had on the people. For supporting resources, go to Regional Civilizations > The Roman Republic and Empire > Roman Origins and Early Political Structures > Explore > The Roman Republic.

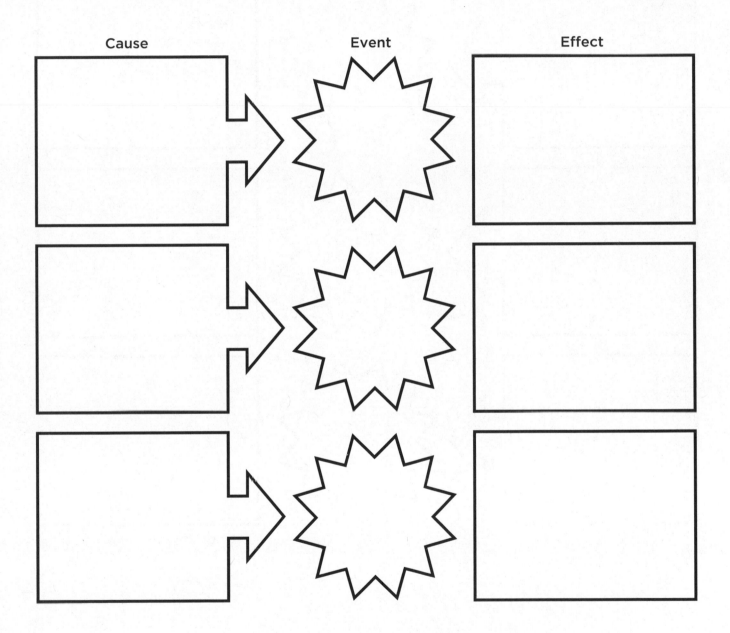

Cause   **Event**   **Effect**

Name _____ Date _____

GRAPHIC ORGANIZER: Cause/Event/Effect Chart (continued)

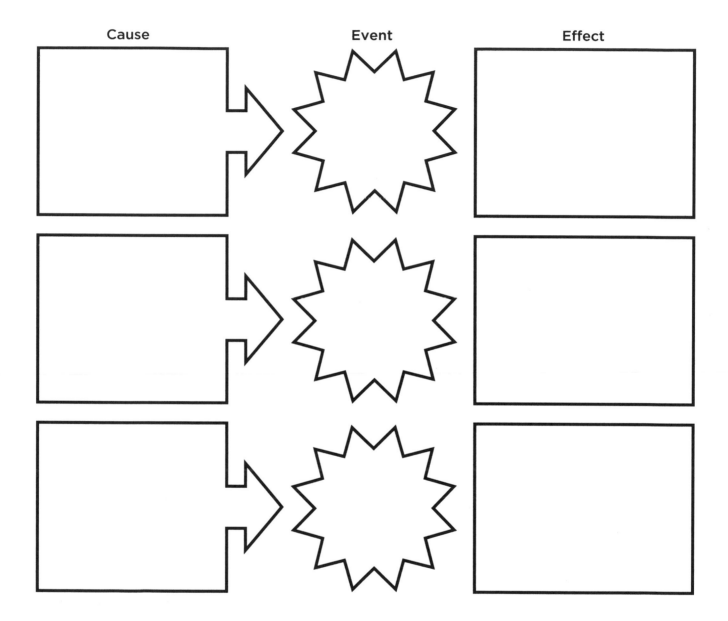

Cause   **Event**   **Effect**

Name _____ **Date** _____

GRAPHIC ORGANIZER: Main Idea Web

Use this Main Idea Web to record the democratic principles used in the government of ancient Rome. For supporting resources, go to Regional Civilizations > The Roman Republic and Empire > Roman Origins and Early Political Structures > Explore > Principles of Democracy.

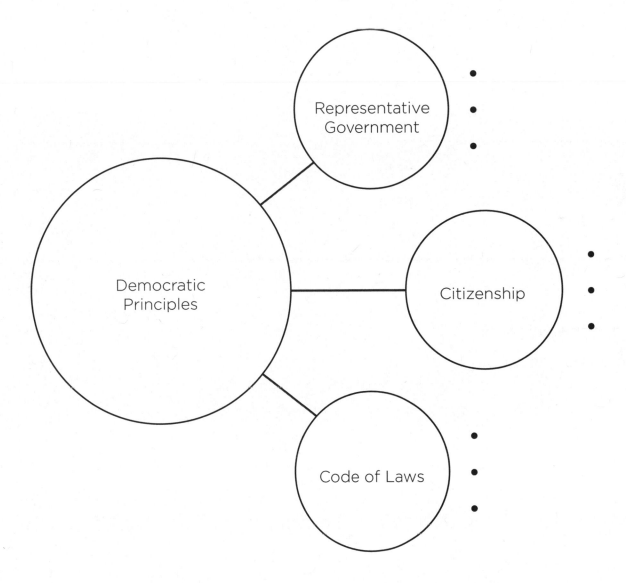

Name _____ **Date** _____

GRAPHIC ORGANIZER: Timeline

Complete this Timeline with the dates of each Punic war, the battle of Zama, and the territory gained. For supporting resources, go to Regional Civilizations > The Roman Republic and Empire > Roman Origins and Early Political Structures > Explore > The Punic Wars.

264 BCE   146 BCE

◆━━━◆

Name _____ Date _____

EXPLORE: FOCUS QUESTIONS

Using what you learned from the Core Interactive Text, answer each page's focus question:

The Roots of Roman Civilization
How did the Roman civilization begin?

_____

_____

_____

The Etruscans
What role did the Etruscans play in Roman history?

_____

_____

_____

The Roman Republic
What form of government was established after the king was removed from power?

_____

_____

_____

Roman Government
What was Rome's political structure?

_____

_____

_____

Principles of Democracy
What democratic principles were present in the government of ancient Rome?

_____

_____

_____

The Punic Wars
What effect did the Punic Wars have on Rome?

_____

_____

_____

PROJECTS AND ASSESSMENTS

Explain Activities

ACTIVITY TYPE: DIAGRAM

Roman Origins and Early Political Structures

Use all the words from the Word Bank to create a graphic answer to the following question: How did different civilizations influence the development of early Roman culture? You may add any other words or symbols to complete your Mind Map. On a separate sheet of paper, summarize your ideas by responding to the statement at the bottom of the Mind Map. Be prepared to present your reasoning.

ACTIVITY TYPE: DIAGRAM

Roman Origins and Early Political Structures

The government of the ancient Roman Republic shares some similarities with the modern United States government. Use the Venn diagram to compare and contrast their characteristics.

ACTIVITY TYPE: SOCIAL STUDIES EXPLANATION

Roman Origins and Early Political Structures

In this Social Studies Explanation activity, you will use a template to assemble evidence from the sources you have explored. Then, you will write an answer to the Essential Question and defend your answer with supporting evidence.

Elaborate Activities

photo:Discovery Education

INVESTIGATION TYPE: HISTORICAL PERSPECTIVES

Roman Society

Your mission is to get to know four individuals from ancient Roman society at the time of the Republic and explore the perspectives you think each would have on key issues of the day.

PROJECTS AND ASSESSMENTS *(continued)*

photo: Library of Congress

ACTIVITY TYPE: CURRENT EVENTS CONNECTION

Ancient Roots of Modern Government

In this activity, you will give a presentation for Constitution Day, a day that celebrates the adoption of the U.S. Constitution. In your presentation, you will discuss the influence of Greek and Roman governments on the U.S. government today.

photo: Library of Congress

ACTIVITY TYPE: ROLE PLAY

Roman Origins and Early Political Structures

In this activity, you will take on the role of either a patrician or a plebeian and write a journal entry describing how you feel about the plebeian struggle for power and equality.

photo: Getty Images

ACTIVITY TYPE: DOCUMENT-BASED INVESTIGATION

Democratic Ideals of Ancient Rome

In this activity, you will write a newspaper article and a speech addressing the people of Rome. In what ways was the civilization of ancient Rome democratic? In what ways was it not democratic?

Evaluate Activities

BRIEF-CONSTRUCTED RESPONSE (BCR)

Roman Origins and Early Political Structures

EXTENDED-CONSTRUCTED RESPONSE (ECR)

Roman Origins and Early Political Structures

UNIT 3: REGIONAL CIVILIZATIONS (2500 BCE TO 1054 CE)

Chapter 10: The Roman Republic and Empire

10.3 From Republic to Empire

photo: Getty Images

LESSON OVERVIEW

Lesson Objectives:

By the end of this lesson, you should be able to:

- **Analyze the causes and effects of Rome's transition from a Republic to an Empire.**
- **Trace the expansion of the Roman Empire from the rise of Caesar to 476 CE.**

Lesson Essential Question:

How did Rome's transition from Republic to Empire impact its citizens?

Key Vocabulary

aqueduct, Brutus, Caligula, Carthage, Charlemagne, citizen, Claudius, Cleopatra VII, consul, dictator, Egypt, Emperor Augustus, Greece, Hannibal, Julius Caesar, Macedonia, Mark Antony, Mediterranean Sea, Middle East, Nero, Octavian, Pax Romana, Ptolemy, Roman Empire, Roman Republic, Rome, Rubicon River, Spain, Tiberius, triumvirate

FLASHCARDS

1 Rome Becomes an Empire

Julius Caesar's defeat of Pompey led to the end of the Roman Republic and the founding of the Roman Empire.

- Caesar was originally Pompey's ally in the First Triumvirate.
- Caesar's victory in Gaul gave him the political strength to defeat Pompey.
- Some members of the Roman Senate were worried about Caesar's growing power and had him assassinated.
- Octavian, Caesar's nephew, won the civil war that followed Caesar's death and became Augustus, the emperor.

Why Does It Matter?

Rome's transformation from a Republic to an Empire meant that the citizens no longer had a say in who ruled them. Instead, the title of emperor was passed down through family lines.

photo: Pixabay

This is a Roman statue of Julius Caesar, who founded the Roman Empire.

2 The Growth of the Empire

The Roman Empire expanded quickly in its first 100 years. Eventually the Empire grew too large to be governed easily.

- Rome's location on the Mediterranean Sea and the warm climate of that location made it easy to expand.
- Conquered nations were absorbed into the Empire. Cities were built to resemble Rome, and the Roman culture was passed on to the new citizens.
- While the Empire itself was run in an orderly fashion, the transfer of the role of emperor involved a great deal of violence and intrigue.

Why Does It Matter?

The Pax Romana brought an end to the internal fighting that had plagued Rome since the time of Caesar. During this period, Rome's expansion brought great wealth and cultural diversity to the Empire and the people living in it. Many people were happy to become a part of Rome because of the many advantages the Romans brought, including better architecture, education, and health. A common language, calendar, religion, and currency helped tie the Empire together.

photo: Getty's Open Content Program

Most of the empire's expansion took place under Augustus and Hadrian.

Name _____ **Date** _____

GRAPHIC ORGANIZER: Sequencing Chart

Use this Sequencing Chart to record events in the rise of the Roman Empire. For supporting resources, go to Regional Civilizations > The Roman Republic and Empire > From Republic to Empire > Explore > The Rise of Julius Caesar.

Event	Date	Summary

Name _____ **Date** _____

GRAPHIC ORGANIZER: Sequencing Chart *(continued)*

Event	Date	Summary

Name _____ **Date** _____

GRAPHIC ORGANIZER: Main Idea Web

Use this Main Idea Web to take notes on the Roman Empire. For supporting resources, go to Regional Civilizations > The Roman Republic and Empire > From Republic to Empire > Explore > Portrait of an Empire.

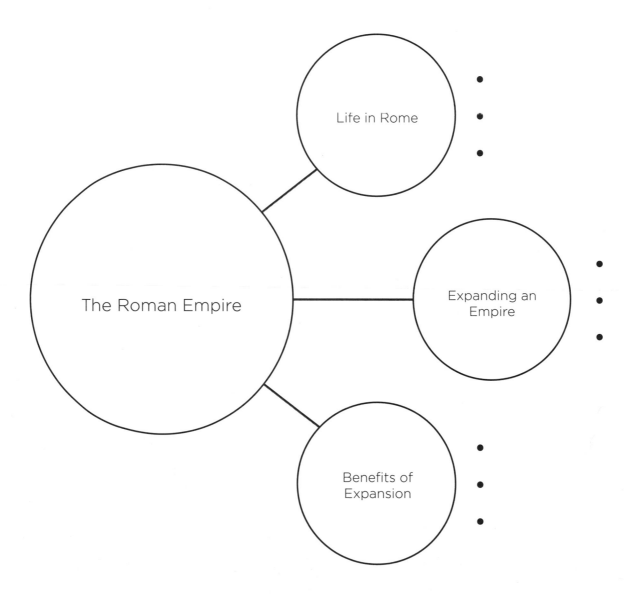

The Roman Empire

Life in Rome

Expanding an Empire

Benefits of Expansion

Name _____ Date _____

EXPLORE: FOCUS QUESTIONS

Using what you learned from the Core Interactive Text, answer each page's focus question:

The Rise of Julius Caesar
How did Julius Caesar come to power?

_____

_____

_____

Dictator for Life
How did Julius Caesar become dictator for life?

_____

_____

_____

The Ides of March
Why was Julius Caesar murdered?

_____

_____

_____

Civil War
How was stability restored to Rome after the death of Julius Caesar?

_____

_____

_____

The Dynastic Tradition
How was power transferred in the Roman Empire?

_____

_____

_____

Name _____ **Date** _____

EXPLORE: FOCUS QUESTIONS *(continued)*

Portrait of an Empire
What was life like in the Roman Empire?

_____
_____
_____
_____

The Empire Grows
How did the Roman Empire expand?

_____
_____
_____
_____

The Benefits of Expansion
How did expansion benefit the Roman Empire?

_____
_____
_____
_____

PROJECTS AND ASSESSMENTS

Explain Activities

ACTIVITY TYPE: MOVIE TRAILER

From Republic to Empire

In this activity, you will use story frames to create a scene from a movie trailer for a new film about the rise and expansion of the Roman Empire.

ACTIVITY TYPE: YOU AS JOURNALIST

From Republic to Empire

In this activity, you will write an informational piece to investigate an event that led to changes in Rome's political system from a republic to an empire, including the cause of the event and the result, or effect, of the event.

ACTIVITY TYPE: SOCIAL STUDIES EXPLANATION

From Republic to Empire

In this Social Studies Explanation activity, you will use a template to assemble evidence from the sources you have explored. Then, you will write an answer to the Essential Question and defend your answer with supporting evidence.

Elaborate Activities

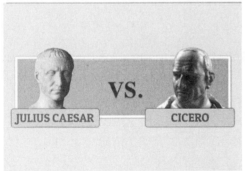

photo: Discovery Education

INVESTIGATION TYPE: ENDURING DEBATE

Julius Caesar vs. Cicero

Is the traditional republican form of government the best way to rule the Roman Empire?

photo: Getty Images

ACTIVITY TYPE: ROLE PLAY

From Republic to Empire

In this activity, you will take on the role of either Octavian or Mark Antony and participate in a mediation session during which you will try to resolve your differences and come to terms with a fellow student playing the part of your rival.

PROJECTS AND ASSESSMENTS *(continued)*

photo: Pixabay

ACTIVITY TYPE: CLASSROOM DEBATE

From Republic to Empire

In this activity, you will learn about the early Roman Empire and determine how the shift from the republican era affected life for ordinary Romans. After you have completed your research, you will participate in a debate.

photo: Getty Images

ACTIVITY TYPE: DOCUMENT-BASED INVESTIGATION

The Real Julius Caesar

In this Document-Based Investigation, you will analyze and synthesize information from a variety of primary and secondary source documents to develop and defend an argument about Julius Caesar's rule over Rome.

Evaluate Activities

BRIEF-CONSTRUCTED RESPONSE (BCR)

From Republic to Empire

EXTENDED-CONSTRUCTED RESPONSE (ECR)

From Republic to Empire

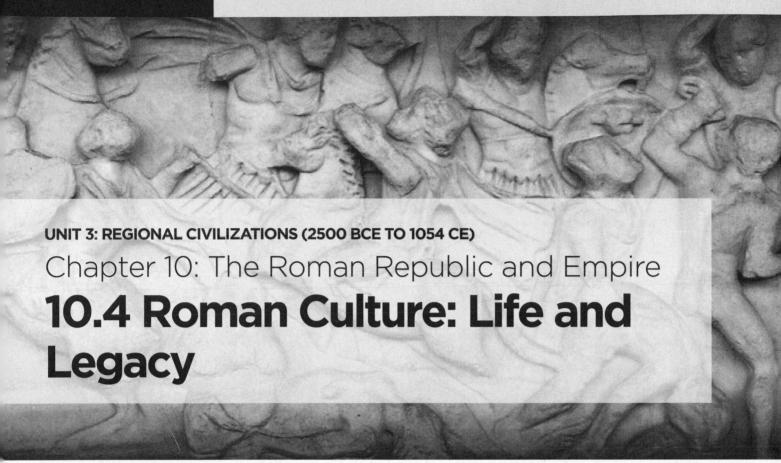

photo: Getty Images

UNIT 3: REGIONAL CIVILIZATIONS (2500 BCE TO 1054 CE)

Chapter 10: The Roman Republic and Empire

10.4 Roman Culture: Life and Legacy

LESSON OVERVIEW

Lesson Objectives:

By the end of this lesson, you should be able to:

- **Analyze relationships of power between Roman rulers, citizens, and slaves.**
- **Analyze the impact of Roman government infrastructure programs on Roman life and culture and on life and culture today.**
- **Trace the influence of the Roman Empire on language.**

Key Vocabulary

aqueduct, architecture, census, Circus Maximus, Colosseum, Egypt, Emperor Augustus, Europe, gladiator, hierarchy, irrigation, Latin, legionnaires, North Africa, Octavian, Pantheon, paterfamilias, patrician, Pax Romana, Phoenicians, plebian, Roman Empire, Rome, Sicily, taxes, Twelve Tables

Lesson Essential Question:

How did the spread of Roman culture influence life throughout the Empire?

FLASHCARDS

1 **Power Relationships in Rome Before the Empire**

Roman society was dominated by men and was very hierarchical, traditional, and family-oriented. The structure of Roman society was mirrored by the structure of the Roman family.

- **During the early republic:**
  - **In the family, the power resided in the hands of the paterfamilias (father of the family); below him were subordinate men, then the women and enslaved persons.**
  - **In a patrician family, there might also be clients, who were plebeians who had pledged loyalty.**
  - **A small group of rich men of the patrician class formed the governing body, the Senate.**
  - **Plebeians were more numerous than patricians but could not participate in government.**
  - **Plebeians fought to gain increased political power and to establish the Twelve Tables, the basic law code of ancient Rome.**
- **After the establishment of the empire:**
  - **Society was still dominated by men, but women had more of a life outside the home.**
  - **Power shifted into the hands of the emperors.**
  - **The number of enslaved people increased until they greatly outnumbered the plebeians, putting the plebeians out of work.**
  - **Emperors employed "bread and circuses" to keep unemployed plebeians from rioting.**
  - **Slavery supported the empire. Enslaved people could buy their freedom on occasion.**
  - **Slave revolts rocked the empire and instilled a long-lasting fear of slavery in the ruling class.**

Why Does It Matter?

The ideas in the Twelve Tables provided the principles of law adopted by the republic and inspired the creators of the French and American democracies. Also, the more Rome exerted its power over the rest of the known world through conquest, the more Roman citizens gave up their own power, until Rome's republic became an empire. Rome never stopped being a hierarchical society with power in the hands of the wealthy few. This division between the classes would lead to later problems.

photo: Library of Congress
The social hierarchy in Rome led to a wide gap between the rich and poor.

FLASHCARDS *(continued)*

2 **Roman Genius**

By developing roads, aqueducts, a common currency, a code of law, and introducing practical reforms, Rome created order over an immense area with an extraordinary diversity of people and languages, which allowed the spread of its cultural achievements.

- Roman engineers and architects develop techniques and styles that are uniquely their own.
- Communal baths spread throughout the empire.
- Invention of concrete explains in part why so many Roman buildings and roads throughout the empire still survive.
- Rome uses Greek building styles but also added its own architectural strategies (vaults, arches, use of concrete) to build larger, taller, and heavier buildings.
- Greco-Roman art strongly influences Renaissance artists.

Why Does It Matter?

Rome's cultural achievements would not have had such a broad impact if Rome had not had a well-developed infrastructure, bureaucracy, and administration. The infrastructure created order. Because of this organization, some cultures actually welcomed conquest because it brought order. In general, Rome did not enslave the conquered peoples; they became citizens and thus could be taxed. Roman cultural achievements were able to spread far and wide because of these conquests. Many of the achievements of Rome still impact our lives today.

photo: Library of Congress

The technological achievements of ancient Rome, such as roads and aqueducts, helped its leaders maintain control over the expanding empire.

3 **The Development of Language**

Latin is a practical language for a practical people. Its ability to absorb the innovations of other cultures and still retain its own identity underlines its continued existence in scientific and legal terminology. Although people do not speak it today, it has had a significant impact on the descendants of the Roman Empire.

- Latin became the common language of the Roman Empire.
- Latin became the official language of the Roman Catholic Church.
- Latin is still used in terminology for law, science, and mathematics. The spread of Latin transformed the languages of European tribes, resulting in the formation of various Romance languages.
- English contains many Latin-based words.
- The Latin alphabet and script became more widespread than any other and became the basis for the modern English alphabet.

Why Does It Matter?

Latin's remarkable resilience and transformation into the common language of the Mediterranean region brought people who spoke different languages closer; it enabled them to communicate across the divides of culture, class, and history.

photo: Library of Congress

The Gutenberg Bible, the first book printed in the Western world, was printed in Latin.

Name _____ **Date** _____

GRAPHIC ORGANIZER: GREASES Chart

Use this GREASES Chart to record characteristics of Roman culture. For supporting resources, go to Regional Civilizations > The Roman Republic and Empire > Roman Culture: Life and Legacy > Explore > Roman Society.

Government	
Religion	
Economic	
Art & Architecture	
Science & Technology	
Environment	
Social & Cultural Values	

Name _____ **Date** _____

GRAPHIC ORGANIZER: Comparison Chart

Use this Comparison Chart to compare and contrast the roles and responsibilities of citizens from various social classes in Rome. For supporting resources, go to Regional Civilizations > The Roman Republic and Empire > Roman Culture: Life and Legacy > Explore > Patrons and Clients.

Criteria	Roles	Responsibilities
Patricians		
Plebians		
Women		
Slaves		

Name _____ Date _____

EXPLORE: FOCUS QUESTIONS

Using what you learned from the Core Interactive Text, answer each page's focus question:

Roman Society

How was Roman society structured?

_____
_____
_____
_____

Patrons and Clients

What was patronage?

_____
_____
_____
_____

Slavery in Ancient Rome

What role did slavery play in the Roman Empire?

_____
_____
_____
_____

Bread and Circuses

How did the ruling classes attempt to keep the poorer members of society happy?

_____
_____
_____
_____

Pax Romana

What led to the Pax Romana?

_____
_____
_____
_____

Name _____ Date _____

EXPLORE: FOCUS QUESTIONS *(continued)*

Moving People, Moving Water
How did public projects impact culture in the Roman Empire?

_____

_____

_____

A Practical Art
What kind of influence has Roman art and architecture had on Western culture?

_____

_____

_____

Latin: Dead or Alive
How did Latin influence the world?

_____

_____

_____

PROJECTS AND ASSESSMENTS

Explain Activities

ACTIVITY TYPE: DIAGRAM

Roman Culture: Life and Legacy

In this activity, you will use a mind map to create a graphic explanation of the structure of power in ancient Roman society, which includes the structure of family power.

ACTIVITY TYPE: YOU AS JOURNALIST

Roman Culture: Life and Legacy

In this activity, you will imagine you live in the city of Smyrna after it has been conquered by Rome.

ACTIVITY TYPE: SOCIAL STUDIES EXPLANATION

Roman Culture: Life and Legacy

In this Social Studies Explanation activity, you will use a template to assemble evidence from the sources you have explored. Then, you will write an answer to the Essential Question and defend your answer with supporting evidence.

Elaborate Activities

photo: Getty Images

INVESTIGATION TYPE: MAP-GUIDED INQUIRY

All Roads Lead to Rome

How did Roman culture spread throughout the provinces of the Roman Empire? What evidence of Roman occupation can still be found today? In this investigation, you will use the Map-Guided Inquiry interactive tool to examine how ancient Roman culture influenced the world around it and continues to affect us today.

photo: Getty Images

ACTIVITY TYPE: PITCH YOUR IDEA

Bid for Bridge Construction

In this activity, you will create a slideshow presentation to deliver before the Roman governor of Spain describing your construction plan and explaining why your company should be the one awarded the project.

PROJECTS AND ASSESSMENTS *(continued)*

photo: Getty's Open Content Program

ACTIVITY TYPE: SAY WHAT?

"Bread and Circuses"

In this activity, you will translate an excerpt from ancient Roman text into modern language, draw or diagram its main idea, and analyze its relevance to the society and culture of ancient Rome.

photo: Getty Images

ACTIVITY TYPE: DOCUMENT-BASED INVESTIGATION

Class Structure in Roman Society

In this activity, you will analyze the roles of the various classes in ancient Roman society and the power that each class had. You will also trace how the classes were affected and changed by developments in Roman culture over time.

Evaluate Activities

BRIEF-CONSTRUCTED RESPONSE (BCR)

Roman Culture: Life and Legacy

EXTENDED-CONSTRUCTED RESPONSE (ECR)

Roman Culture: Life and Legacy

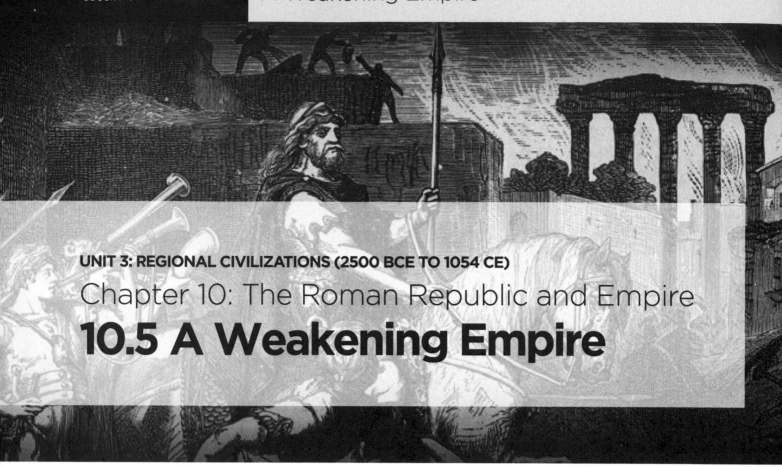

UNIT 3: REGIONAL CIVILIZATIONS (2500 BCE TO 1054 CE)

Chapter 10: The Roman Republic and Empire

10.5 A Weakening Empire

LESSON OVERVIEW

Lesson Objectives:

By the end of this lesson, you should be able to:

- Analyze and explain the political, geographic, and cultural factors that led to the fall of the Roman Empire.
- Explain how Constantine's establishment of the new capital in Constantinople helped lead to the Western Empire's fall.
- Describe the sack of Rome and analyze the impact of the dismantling of the empire.

Lesson Essential Question:

Why did Rome decline and fall?

Key Vocabulary

Alaric, Attila, Battle of Adrianople, Byzantine Empire, Catholicism / Roman Catholicism, Celtic peoples, Christianity, citizen, Constantine, Constantinople, Diocletian, Division of the Roman Empire, Eastern Orthodox Christianity, empire, Gaul, Germanic peoples, Goths, Huns, migration, nomadic, province, Roman Empire, Roman Senate, Rome, Spain, taxes, technology, trade

FLASHCARDS

1 Decline

After the year 180, political, geographic, and cultural factors led the Roman Empire into gradual weakness and eventual collapse.

- For nearly a century, Rome had no orderly transfer of power as emperors replaced one another by force, bribery, and murder.
- Leaders gave no thought to the general welfare of the state but sought power only to enrich themselves.
- High taxes to pay for the army and for bribes to enemy leaders drove Romans into poverty and crippled trade.
- Migration of the Huns, a nomadic people of Asia, frightened the Germanic tribes and drove them toward Roman territory.

Why Does It Matter?

Rome was the most powerful state the world had known to that time, but its power was undermined by forces inside and outside the empire.

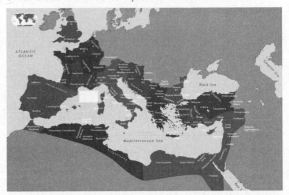

photo: Discovery Education
The constant warfare of the 200s crippled the economy of the Roman Empire.

2 Diocletian and Constantine

After Diocletian restored order and organization, Constantine radically changed the structure of the empire.

- Diocletian restored order to the empire and reorganized the government.
- Diocletian gave up his throne, and his new government fell.
- Constantine won the struggle for power that followed Diocletian's rule and appointed himself emperor.
- Constantine saw that the city of Rome itself was no longer important to the life of the empire.
- Constantine moved the capital of the empire from Rome to a new city, which he named for himself.
- The Western Roman Empire was heavily taxed to pay for defense of the east and was left without adequate defenses against the Germanic tribes.

Why Does It Matter?

The Eastern Roman Empire remained intact during the barbarian invasions, while the Western Empire collapsed.

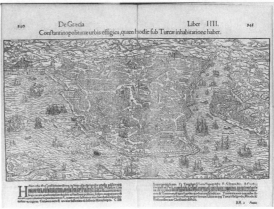

photo: Library of Congress
How did Constantine's decision to found a new capital lead to the decline of the city of Rome and of Rome itself?

FLASHCARDS *(continued)*

3 ▸ Fall

The city of Rome was sacked several times by Germanic tribes, and the empire broke apart.

- Alaric the Goth was the first Germanic king to sack Rome, in 410.
- The invasion of the empire by the Huns, under their leader Attila, eventually caused the Germanic tribes to break up the empire.
- Odoacer, another Gothic chieftain, deposed the last Roman emperor in the west in 476.
- After the fall of the Western Roman Empire, Europe was broken into separate kingdoms, most ruled by Germanic tribes.
- Roman cultural traditions were lost as Western Europe sank into its "Dark Ages."
- The Eastern Roman Empire survived as the Byzantine Empire until 1453.

Why Does It Matter?

The destruction of a strong political and cultural tradition led to centuries of disorder and hardship until new traditions evolved.

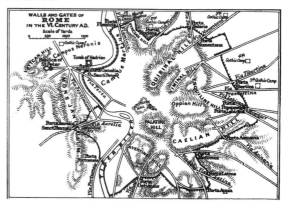

photo: Procopius. History of the Wars. Vol. 3. Trans. H. B. Dewing. New York, NY: G. P. Putnam's Sons, 1919.

Despite many walls and gates, the Roman Empire was invaded several times.

Name _____ Date _____

GRAPHIC ORGANIZER: GREASES Chart

Use this GREASES Chart to record information about Roman society in the period before and during the empire's decline and fall. For supporting resources, go to Regional Civilizations > The Roman Republic and Empire > A Weakening Empire > Explore > Who Was Emperor? Who Was Not Emperor?

Government	
Religion	
Economic	
Art & Architecture	
Science & Technology	
Environment	
Social & Cultural Values	

SOCIAL STUDIES TECHBOOK

Discovery EDUCATION

Name _____ **Date** _____

GRAPHIC ORGANIZER: Cause/Event/Effect Chart

Use this Cause/Event/Effect Chart to list the causes and effects of each event related to the decline and fall of the Roman Empire. For supporting resources, go to Regional Civilizations > The Roman Republic and Empire > A Weakening Empire > Explore > Attacks from the East.

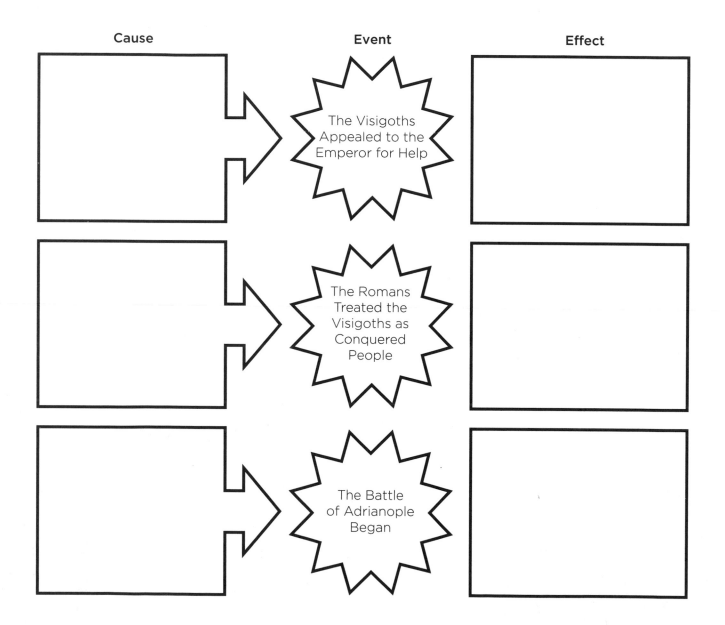

Cause   Event   Effect

The Visigoths Appealed to the Emperor for Help

The Romans Treated the Visigoths as Conquered People

The Battle of Adrianople Began

Name _____ **Date** _____

GRAPHIC ORGANIZER: Cause/Event/Effect Chart *(continued)*

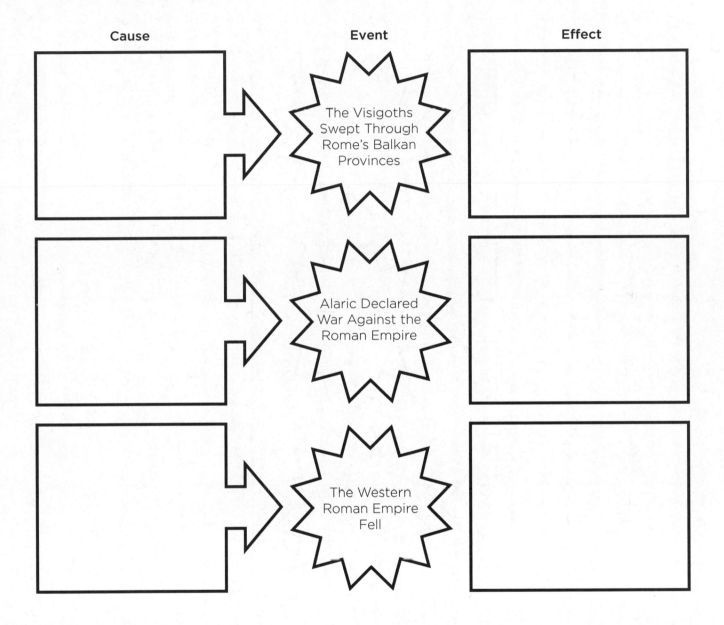

Cause   Event   Effect

The Visigoths Swept Through Rome's Balkan Provinces

Alaric Declared War Against the Roman Empire

The Western Roman Empire Fell

SOCIAL STUDIES TECHBOOK

Name _____ **Date** _____

GRAPHIC ORGANIZER: Cause/Event/Effect Chart *(continued)*

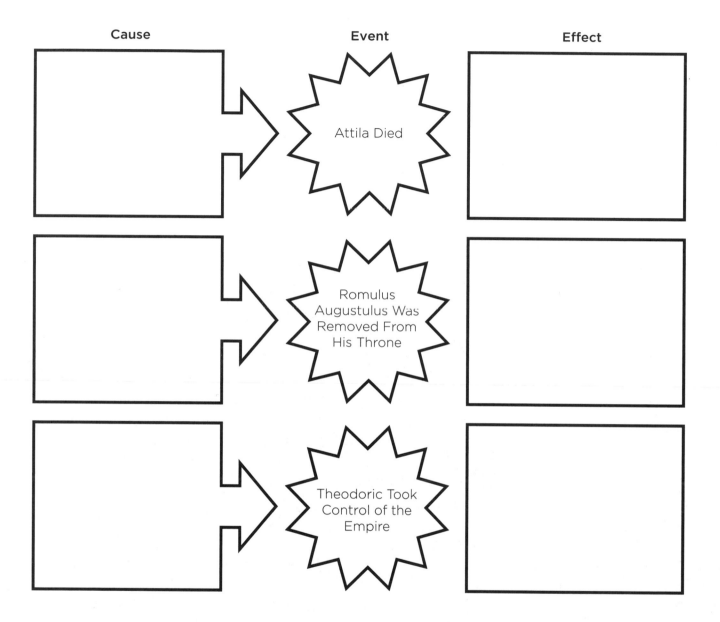

Cause   **Event**   **Effect**

Attila Died

Romulus Augustulus Was Removed From His Throne

Theodoric Took Control of the Empire

Name _____ Date _____

EXPLORE: FOCUS QUESTIONS

Using what you learned from the Core Interactive Text, answer each page's focus question:

Who Was Emperor? Who Was Not Emperor?
How did Rome become politically unstable?

_____

_____

_____

Chaos in the Armies
How did internal conflict weaken the empire?

_____

_____

_____

Beyond the Frontier
Who were the barbarian tribes?

_____

_____

_____

The Empire Divided
Why was the capital of the Roman Empire moved?

_____

_____

_____

The Empire in the East
How did Constantinople become Rome's second capital?

_____

_____

_____

Name _____ **Date** _____

EXPLORE: FOCUS QUESTIONS *(continued)*

Attacks from the East
Why did Germanic tribes attack Rome?

_____
_____
_____
_____

The Fall of Rome
How did Rome fall to Germanic tribes?

_____
_____
_____
_____

After the Fall of Rome
What happened after the fall of the Western Roman Empire?

_____
_____
_____

PROJECTS AND ASSESSMENTS

Explain Activities

ACTIVITY TYPE: VISUALIZATION

A Weakening Empire

Choose the most important events or trends that contributed to the decline and fall of the Roman Empire. Diagram the events or trends in order of their importance, from the sixth-most important to the most important overall. Add a title, illustrate the events or trends, and justify your ranking below each illustration with a caption.

ACTIVITY TYPE: YOU AS JOURNALIST

A Weakening Empire

In this activity, you will interview an eyewitness to the events leading to the decline and fall of the Roman Empire.

ACTIVITY TYPE: SOCIAL STUDIES EXPLANATION

A Weakening Empire

In this Social Studies Explanation activity, you will use a template to assemble evidence from the sources you have explored. Then, you will write an answer to the Essential Question and defend your answer with supporting evidence.

Elaborate Activities

photo: Getty Images

INVESTIGATION TYPE: TIMELINE MAP

The Harder They Fall

Was Rome destroyed by outside enemies or by weakness within the empire itself? Your mission is to explore the events leading up to the fall of the Western Roman Empire, from 180 to 476, and identify the main reasons for Rome's fall.

PROJECTS AND ASSESSMENTS *(continued)*

photo: Library of Congress

ACTIVITY TYPE: CLASSROOM SPEECH

Addressing the Roman Senate

In this activity, you will prepare a speech for delivery to the Senate on how the actions of the armies are weakening the empire and what you believe should be done about it.

photo: Library of Congress

ACTIVITY TYPE: PITCH YOUR IDEA

Learning from the Past

In this activity, you will use the example of Rome and at least one other ancient empire to create and deliver a proposal to a modern ruler.

photo: Getty Images

ACTIVITY TYPE: DOCUMENT-BASED INVESTIGATION

A Weakening Empire

In this Document-Based Investigation, you will analyze source materials and investigate this question: In a recent scholarly article, Professor Know-It-All claimed that during his reign, "Emperor Constantine I did more harm than good to the declining Roman Empire." Did he or didn't he?

Evaluate Activities

BRIEF-CONSTRUCTED RESPONSE (BCR)

A Weakening Empire

EXTENDED-CONSTRUCTED RESPONSE (ECR)

A Weakening Empire

Discovery EDUCATION | SOCIAL STUDIES TECHBOOK

UNIT 3: REGIONAL CIVILIZATIONS (2500 BCE TO 1054 CE)

Chapter 11: Origins and Growth of Christianity

11.1 Christianity: Origins and Characteristics

photo: Getty's Open Content Program

LESSON OVERVIEW

Lesson Objectives:

By the end of this lesson, you should be able to:

- Explain the origins of Christianity based on the life and teachings of Jesus.
- Describe the characteristics of Christianity.

Lesson Essential Question:

How did Christianity develop?

Key Vocabulary

Abraham, apostle, beginning of Christianity, Bethlehem, bishop, Christianity, Constantine, Hebrews, Herod the Great, Israel, Jerusalem, Jesus, Judaism, Judea, King David, King Solomon, Mecca, Messiah, missionary, monotheism, Moses, Muhammad, Nazareth, Nebuchadnezzar, New Testament, Palestine, parable, Phoenicians, polytheism, proselytizing religion / universalizing religion, Roman Empire, Rome, Ruth, Saul, Ten Commandments

FLASHCARDS

1 The Life and Teachings of Jesus

Christians believe that Jesus Christ lived and taught in Israel at the start of the Common Era.

- Israel was under the control of the Roman Empire.
- The life and teachings of Jesus are written in the Gospels of the four apostles: Matthew, Mark, Luke, and John.
- Love of God and compassion for other people are the primary rules of Christianity.
- Christians believe that Jesus died and was resurrected.
- Christianity was outlawed by the Roman Empire until Emperor Constantine made it the official religion in the 200s.

Why Does It Matter?

The origins of Christianity in Roman-controlled Judea and the story behind the life and teachings of Jesus are crucial to understanding how Christianity became such a widespread religion.

photo: Library of Congress

This painting is an artist's depiction of Jesus's resurrection.

2 Characteristics of Christianity

Christianity is the belief that Jesus Christ was the human son of God and that he died to redeem the sins of humanity.

- The Christian Bible includes both the Old Testament and the New Testament.
- Christians believe in the same God as the Jews. They follow some Jewish laws, like the Ten Commandments, but not others.
- Many Christians proselytize, or actively try to convert people to Christianity.

Why Does It Matter?

Christianity developed out of Judaism and kept some of its laws and customs. The Christian practice of proselytizing has helped make it one of the largest and most diverse religions in the world.

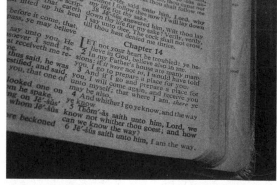

photo: Pixabay

The Old Testament of the Christian Bible contains many of the same biblical books as the Jewish Torah. The New Testament is exclusive to the Christian Bible.

Name _____ **Date** _____

GRAPHIC ORGANIZER: Sequencing Chart

Use this Sequencing Chart to create a timeline of the life of Jesus. For supporting resources, go to Regional Civilizations > Origins and Growth of Christianity > Christianity: Origins and Characteristics > Explore > The Birth of Jesus.

Event	Importance to Religion

Name _____ Date _____

EXPLORE: FOCUS QUESTIONS

Using what you learned from the Core Interactive Text, answer each page's focus question:

Judea Under Roman Rule
What was Judea like when Christianity began to develop?

_____
_____
_____
_____

The Birth of Jesus
What do Christians believe about the birth of Jesus?

_____
_____
_____
_____

Who Was Jesus?
What do Christians believe about Jesus's life?

_____
_____
_____
_____

Jesus's Teachings
What were the teachings of Jesus?

_____
_____
_____
_____

Building the Bible
What was included in the Christian Bible?

_____
_____
_____
_____

Spreading the Faith
How did Christianity spread?

_____
_____
_____

© Discovery Education | www.DiscoveryEducation.com

PROJECTS AND ASSESSMENTS

Explain Activities

ACTIVITY TYPE: DIAGRAM

Christianity: Origins and Characteristics

In this activity, you will use a 3-Way Venn Diagram to compare the major beliefs of two ancient religions, or belief systems, with Christianity.

ACTIVITY TYPE: DIAGRAM

Christianity: Origins and Characteristics

In this activity, you will use at least 10 words from the word bank to create a mind map graphic response to the Essential Question.

ACTIVITY TYPE: SOCIAL STUDIES EXPLANATION

Christianity: Origins and Characteristics

In this Social Studies Explanation activity, you will use a template to assemble evidence from the sources you have explored. Then, you will write an answer to the Essential Question and defend your answer with supporting evidence.

Elaborate Activities

photo: Getty Images

INVESTIGATION TYPE: SOURCE ANALYSIS

Tenets of Christianity

How did stained glass windows in medieval churches help teach the basic tenets of Christianity through allegorical scenes from the Bible or Gospels? In this investigation, you will analyze a stained glass window and find evidence of how these works of art were used to advance the Christian faith.

photo: Library of Congress

ACTIVITY TYPE: SAY WHAT?

The Sermon on the Mount

In this activity, you will translate excerpts from the Sermon on the Mount into modern language.

PROJECTS AND ASSESSMENTS *(continued)*

photo: Getty's Open Content Program

ACTIVITY TYPE: DOCUMENT-BASED INVESTIGATION

Christianity: Origins and Characteristics

In this Document-Based Investigation, you will be analyzing the interactions between early Christians and the Romans. As you analyze the sources, investigate this question: Why did Roman officials persecute Christians?

Evaluate Activities

BRIEF-CONSTRUCTED RESPONSE (BCR)

Christianity: Origins and Characteristics

EXTENDED-CONSTRUCTED RESPONSE (ECR)

Christianity: Origins and Characteristics

UNIT 3: REGIONAL CIVILIZATIONS (2500 BCE TO 1054 CE)

Chapter 11: Origins and Growth of Christianity
11.2 Christianity's Spread

photo: Getty Images

LESSON OVERVIEW

Lesson Objectives:

By the end of this lesson, you should be able to:

- Analyze the factors that led to the diffusion of Christianity throughout the Roman Empire and other parts of Europe.
- Explain the importance of monks, missionaries, and the Christian church itself in the spread of Christianity throughout Europe.
- Describe the impact of the fall of the Western Roman Empire on Christianity.

Key Vocabulary

bishop, Catholic Church, Christianity, Constantine, convert, disciple, missionary, monastery, monk, Paul, pope, propaganda, proselytizing religion / universalizing religion, Saint Anthony, Saint Patrick

Lesson Essential Question:

How did Christianity become the world's largest religion?

FLASHCARDS

1 The Diffusion of Christianity

Christianity spread throughout the Roman Empire and other parts of Europe for a number of reasons and with a variety of results.

- After Jesus's death, his disciples spread his word and convinced others to become Christians.
- Because Christians put God before the emperor, they were persecuted by Roman officials.
- Christianity's message of equality, hope, and salvation made it appealing to many, especially those in the lower classes.
- As Rome's culture spread, so did Christianity.
- Roman Emperor Constantine adopted Christianity in 312, ending the persecution of Christians.

Why Does It Matter?

Christianity overcame many obstacles to become a popular religion. Early worshipers suffered persecution and harassment for their beliefs until Christianity became widespread. Today, early adopters of radical ideas often endure public scrutiny and criticism until their ideas become accepted.

photo: IRC

Steles like this commemorated important events in Roman life. This one shows a Christian being immersed in water to be baptized.

2 Key Players in the Spread of Christianity

Monks, missionaries, and the Christian church itself were important in the spread of Christianity throughout Europe.

- Missionaries traveled to areas where people were not Christian and convinced them to join their faith.
- Monasteries were communities for monks who dedicated their lives to prayer and service to God.
- Christianity spread from Jerusalem into Syria, Egypt, and elsewhere, until most Roman citizens were Christian.

Why Does It Matter?

The Christian religion spread rapidly. Some believers moved around to find new converts, and some servants of the church stayed in their communities to serve worshipers there. Missionaries are still active around the world, working to convert others to Christianity.

photo: Library of Congress

This is a figure of a monk.

FLASHCARDS *(continued)*

3 ▶ **The Church Splits**

By 1054, Christianity had spread across Europe, parts of Asia, and parts of Africa. But disagreements over how Christianity should be practiced splintered the church.

- **Church leaders in the East and West disagreed over how much power the pope should have.**
- **In 1054, the Christian church split.**
- **The Orthodox Church rose in the East.**
- **The Catholic Church rose in the West.**

Why Does It Matter?

Disagreements over church practices still exist in the Christian church. The church has several different denominations, or subgroups, that view and practice Christianity in different ways.

photo: Pixabay
After the schism, the Eastern Orthodox church developed its own traditions and thrived.

Name _____ **Date** _____

GRAPHIC ORGANIZER: Comparison Chart

Use this Cause/Event/Effect Chart to explore the different factors that affected the spread of Christianity. For supporting resources, go to Regional Civilizations > Origins and Growth of Christianity > Christianity's Spread > Explore > Disciples Spread the Story.

Criteria:	Who?	How/Why?
Spreading Christianity		
Converting to Christianity		
Opposing Christianity		

Name _____ **Date** _____

GRAPHIC ORGANIZER: Venn Diagram

Use this Venn Diagram to compare and contrast the Eastern Orthodox Church and the Roman Catholic Church. For supporting resources, go to Regional Civilizations > Origins and Growth of Christianity > Christianity's Spread > Explore > The Church Splits.

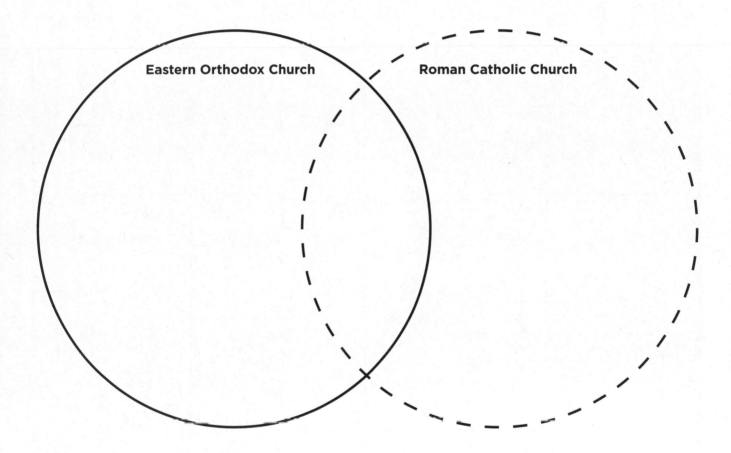

Eastern Orthodox Church

Roman Catholic Church

Name _____ **Date** _____

GRAPHIC ORGANIZER: Vocabulary Chart

Use this Vocabulary Chart to define the word *schism*. For supporting resources, go to Regional Civilizations > Origins and Growth of Christianity > Christianity's Spread > Explore > The Church Splits.

DEFINITION:

Personal:

Dictionary:

EXAMPLES (Drawn or Written):

TERM:
schism

SENTENCES:

Teacher/Book:

Personal:

RELATED:

WORD PARTS:

Outside of School (Who Would Use the Word? How Would He or She Use It?):

© Discovery Education | www.DiscoveryEducation.com

Name _____ Date _____

EXPLORE: FOCUS QUESTIONS

Using what you learned from the Core Interactive Text, answer each page's focus question:

Disciples Spread the Story
Who spread Christianity after Jesus died?

_____

_____

_____

Suffering for Beliefs
How and why were Christians persecuted for their beliefs?

_____

_____

_____

The Emperor Constantine Adopts Christianity
How did Constantine influence Christianity?

_____

_____

_____

Monks and Monasteries Help Christianity Expand
How did monks help Christianity grow into the world's largest religion?

_____

_____

_____

Christianity Spreads After the Empire Falls
How did the fall of the Roman Empire affect Christianity?

_____

_____

_____

The Church Splits
How did the East-West Schism lead to two separate Christian churches?

_____

_____

_____

PROJECTS AND ASSESSMENTS

Explain Activities

ACTIVITY TYPE: DIAGRAM

Spread of Christianity

In the main idea web, identify three factors that led to the spread of Christianity throughout the Roman Empire and other parts of Europe.

ACTIVITY TYPE: YOU AS JOURNALIST

Christianity's Spread

In this activity, you will write an article that follows one of these headlines: "Little-Known Religion of Christianity Now Spreading Throughout the Empire," "Religion Spreads Despite Persecution," or "Emperor Embraces New Faith."

ACTIVITY TYPE: SOCIAL STUDIES EXPLANATION

Christianity's Spread

In this Social Studies Explanation activity, you will use a template to assemble evidence from the sources you have explored. Then, you will write an answer to the Essential Question and defend your answer with supporting evidence.

Elaborate Activities

photo: Getty Images

INVESTIGATION TYPE: TIMELINE MAP

A New Religion Takes Wing

How did Christianity become the most common religion in medieval Europe? In this investigation, you will use the Timeline Map interactive tool to examine how Christianity grew from a small Middle Eastern sect to one of the most widespread religions in the medieval world.

photo: Getty Images

ACTIVITY TYPE: CURRENT EVENTS CONNECTION

Christianity: Past and Present

In this activity, you will consider the issues that resulted in the schism between the Eastern and Western Christian churches in 1054 CE.

PROJECTS AND ASSESSMENTS *(continued)*

photo: Library of Congress

ACTIVITY TYPE: ROLE PLAY

Early Monks: Their Life and Legacy

In this activity, you will work with a partner to prepare an interview in which you will take turns role-playing the interviewer and interview subject.

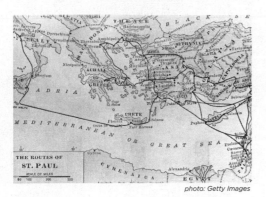

photo: Getty Images

ACTIVITY TYPE: DOCUMENT-BASED INVESTIGATION

Christianity's Spread

In this Document-Based Investigation, you will analyze source materials and investigate this question: What role did women play in the spread of Christianity in the Roman Empire?

Evaluate Activities

BRIEF-CONSTRUCTED RESPONSE (BCR)

Christianity's Spread

EXTENDED-CONSTRUCTED RESPONSE (ECR)

Christianity's Spread

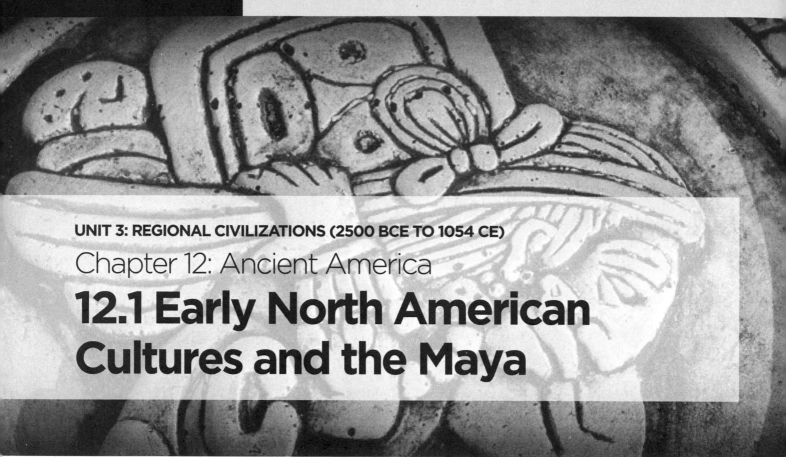

photo: Getty Images

UNIT 3: REGIONAL CIVILIZATIONS (2500 BCE TO 1054 CE)

Chapter 12: Ancient America

12.1 Early North American Cultures and the Maya

LESSON OVERVIEW

Lesson Objectives:

By the end of this lesson, you should be able to:

- **Locate the physical features and early American civilizations on a map of the Americas.**

- **Describe how the geography of the region shaped the way of life of the people living there.**

- **Describe Mayan culture and scientific innovations.**

Lesson Essential Question:

How did physical geography shape the early societies of the Americas?

Key Vocabulary

Amazon River, Andes, Atlantic Ocean, Aztec, Central Plateau, Chichén Itzá, Christopher Columbus, Classic Period, climate, codex, colonization, conquistador, Copan, Egypt, Inca, indentured servant, infrastructure, La Venta, maize, Maya, mestizo, Mexico, Middle America, Nile River, Northwest Passage, Olmec, Peru, polytheism, South America, stela, steppe, terrace farming, Toltec, treaty, Yucatán Peninsula, ziggurat

© Discovery Education | www.DiscoveryEducation.com

FLASHCARDS

1 ▸ Geography of the Americas

Pre-Columbian peoples lived throughout the continents of North and South America and in Central America.

- **The Maya lived in the highlands of southern Mexico and the lowlands of Central America.**
- **Mound-building peoples lived in North America.**
- **Cliff dwellers lived in the southwestern United States.**

Why Does It Matter?

The geography of the Americas played an important role in the development of the early people who settled there. As each people adapted to its environment, unique cultures developed. These cultures gave rise to the tribes found by the Europeans when they came to the Americas.

photo: Pixabay

Fertile farmland for growing crops in the Americas helped make agriculture an important part of the civilizations that developed there.

2 ▸ The Mayan Empire

The development of the Mayan culture was shaped by the geography and climate of Central America and Mexico.

- **The Olmec were cultural ancestors of the Maya.**
- **The Maya built a large road system connecting them to other cities and civilizations.**
- **Mayan farmers practiced terraced agriculture. Crops included corn, cacao beans, and rubber.**
- **Each Mayan city was ruled by a separate leader, and they often fought each other.**
- **The Maya developed a complex calendar system, a number system, a writing system, and a language that influenced modern languages still spoken in Central America and Mexico.**

Why Does It Matter?

The Maya developed many of their unique characteristics because of their geographical location.

photo: Jupiterimages Corporation

The Maya built cities throughout Central America and Mexico, where these city ruins are located.

FLASHCARDS *(continued)*

3 **Culture and Innovations of the Maya**

The Maya developed and improved upon a number of innovations in the areas of math, astronomy, and language.

- The Maya developed a very accurate system of two intersecting calendars. Other Mesoamerican societies adopted this system.
- The Maya adapted a number system originally developed by the Zapotec, which used only three symbols but could be used to solve complex equations.
- The Maya built palaces, sculptures, and observatories used for astronomy.
- The Maya kept written records on stone stelae and codices.
- Variations of the original Mayan languages are spoken by many people in Central America today.

Why Does It Matter?

The central location of the Mayan people, along with the warm and fertile climate, allowed them to share both goods and ideas with neighboring peoples. This also allowed their innovations to survive.

photo: Pixabay

A stone carving shows the written language of the ancient Maya.

Name _____ Date _____

GRAPHIC ORGANIZER: Map of South America

Use this Map to label and describe geographic features in Mesoamerica. For supporting resources, go to Regional Civilizations > Ancient America > Early North American Cultures and the Maya > Explore > Geography of Mesoamerica.

Name _____ **Date** _____

 ## GRAPHIC ORGANIZER: Three-Way Venn Diagram

Use this Three-Way Venn Diagram to compare the Maya with the Ancestral Pueblo (Anasazi) and Cahokia (mound builders). For supporting resources, go to Regional Civilizations > Ancient America > Early North American Cultures and the Maya > Explore > Nations of the Pre-Columbian Americas.

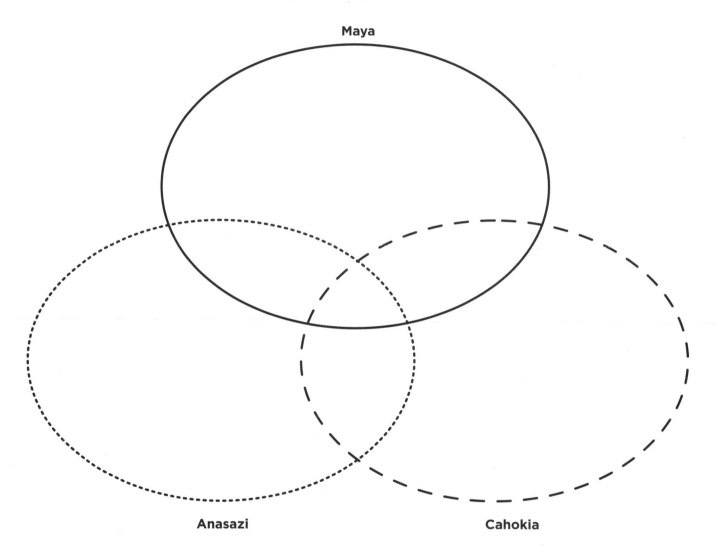

Maya

Anasazi

Cahokia

© Discovery Education | www.DiscoveryEducation.com

Name _____ Date _____

GRAPHIC ORGANIZER: GREASES Chart

Use this GREASES Chart to record details about the Mayan civilization. For supporting resources, go to Regional Civilizations > Ancient America > Early North American Cultures and the Maya > Explore > Mayan Agriculture.

	What I See	My Conclusions
Government		
Religion		
Economic		
Art & Architecture		
Science & Technology		
Environment		
Social & Cultural Values		

Name _____ Date _____

EXPLORE: FOCUS QUESTIONS

Using what you learned from the Core Interactive Text, answer each page's focus question:

Geography of Mesoamerica

What are the important geographical features of the Americas?

_____
_____
_____

Nations of the Pre-Columbian Americas

How did the Toltec and Olmec influence Mesoamerican culture?

_____
_____
_____

Ancient Builders

How did geography shape the development of early North American people?

_____
_____
_____

The Maya

What were the characteristics of the Mayan civilization?

_____
_____
_____

Mayan Agriculture

What role did agriculture play in the Mayan civilization?

_____
_____
_____

Mayan Religion

What was the religious culture of the Maya?

_____
_____
_____

Name _____ Date _____

EXPLORE: FOCUS QUESTIONS *(continued)*

A Decentralized Nation
How did the Maya organize their society?

_____

_____

_____

A Society of Thinkers
What scientific innovations did the Maya develop?

_____

_____

_____

Language and Math
What cultural innovations did the Mayan civilization develop?

_____

_____

_____

PROJECTS AND ASSESSMENTS

Explain Activities

ACTIVITY TYPE: DIAGRAM

Comparing Civilizations

In this activity, you will use a Venn diagram to compare and contrast the Olmec civilization with one of the four early river valley civilizations (Nile, Tigris-Euphrates, Indus, or Yellow). On the back, write a short paragraph describing the similarities and differences between the Olmec and your chosen civilization.

ACTIVITY TYPE: QUICK WRITE

Mayan Innovations

In this activity, you will create an advertisement for one of the ancient Mayan innovations or contributions.

ACTIVITY TYPE: VISUALIZATION

Mesoamerican Geography

In this Visualization activity, you choose a major geographical feature for the Anasazi, Cahokian, and Maya, and then explain how the geographic feature helped define each society.

ACTIVITY TYPE: SOCIAL STUDIES EXPLANATION

Early North American Cultures and the Maya

In this Social Studies Explanation activity, you will use a template to assemble evidence from the sources you have explored. Then, you will write an answer to the Essential Question and defend your answer with supporting evidence.

Elaborate Activities

photo: Getty Images

INVESTIGATION TYPE: SOURCE ANALYSIS

The Mayan Calendars

What role did the Mayan calendars play in the daily lives of people? Analyze the Haab calendar and its importance in the lives of the Maya people.

PROJECTS AND ASSESSMENTS *(continued)*

photo: IRC

ACTIVITY TYPE: PITCH YOUR IDEA

Math of the Maya

In this activity, you will create a presentation to give before a foreign leader explaining how the mathematical innovations of the ancient Maya could improve his kingdom.

photo: Getty Images

ACTIVITY TYPE: STUDENT SLEUTH

Mayan Ball Games

In this activity, you will analyze photographs of ball courts and players, a myth about ball games, and descriptions of the game. Then, you will write the narrative script for the section of the documentary on Mayan ball games, in which you describe the game and its purposes.

photo: Paul Fuqua

ACTIVITY TYPE: DOCUMENT-BASED INVESTIGATION

Mayan Beliefs

In this activity, you will create an exhibit for a museum (or online museum) that shows visitors what Mayan beliefs and rituals reveal about their geography and society. Or, you can create a documentary in which you identify what Mayan beliefs and rituals reveal about their geography and society.

Evaluate Activities

BRIEF-CONSTRUCTED RESPONSE (BCR)

Early North American Cultures and the Maya

EXTENDED-CONSTRUCTED RESPONSE (ECR)

Early North American Cultures and the Maya

Notes